Raising Anti-Diet Kids:

A Parent's Actionable Guide to Ditch Diets and Cultivate Body Respect

Andrea Dow

Raising Anti-Diet Kids, Andrea Dow- 1st ed.

Paperback: 979-8-9877944-0-1

Hardcover: 979-8-9877944-1-8

Ebook: 979-8-9877944-2-5

Cover artwork by Julia, Evie, and Leo Dow

For my six kids who are a constant source of inspiration.

Contents

Section 4
Common Parenting Pitfalls

Section 5
Navigating a Diet-Obsessed World

Section 6
Managing Relationships in the Age of Diet Culture

Section 7
Caring for Your Body

Section 8
Managing Feelings and Mindset

Section 9
Diet Proofing Your Home

Preface

I want you to take a step back in time. Reflect back to your childhood and your relationship with your parents.

Did you look to them for advice, support, love, and an understanding of the world around you? Did they model what you thought was the "right" way to act, dress, or eat? Did you follow their rules and believe what they taught you? Did they spend time allowing you space to explore and follow your instincts? Did they emphasize the importance of trusting yourself and your body?

Whether we like it or not, how we were parented influences our choices throughout life. For some of us that means striving to emulate our parents into adulthood, and for others that can mean aiming to do things completely differently than they did. While my parents certainly weren't perfect, they came pretty close to ticking all the "good" parent boxes in my eyes.

As a kid, I remember thinking my mom was a "good" mom because she always bought us low-sugar cereal and wheat bread. She explained to me that these foods were more nutritious than high-sugar cereals or white bread, and I felt a quiet sense of confidence that we'd never have what I believed was "low-quality" Wonder Bread with those happy red, yellow, and blue circles in our shopping cart.

Not long into my parenting gig, I realized being a mother is so much more nuanced than the type of bread you toss in the cart at the grocery store. There truly is no perfect mom, no right choice of cereal. I started to see how even my own mother was doing the best she could in a system that had her focused on the wrong outcomes steeped in diet culture and fatphobia.

It's not just the right cereal or bread that today's "good" mom is supposed to worry about. In our body-obsessed society, she needs to spend hours scouring the internet for the healthiest recipes, sift through books and articles about the latest food news, make careful substitutions for family recipes, examine food labels like a detective, and monitor her kids' intake like a security guard. Are you serving the right gluten-free, low-sugar, high-energy, protein-dense dinners? Is your body and your kid's body matching the societal ideal of healthy and acceptable, aka thin? Could you be doing more, more, more? It's maddening.

My guess is that, like me, you're trying to do what's best for your kids. Maybe you have stacks of parenting and wellness-expert books on your nightstand, subscriptions to parenting and health newsletters and blogs, a podcast app featuring the best tips and strategies for improving your kids' (and your own) lives, and an attentive ear that listens to advice from friends, family, doctors, and school to gain the latest morsel of information that will help your child be healthier, happier, or more successful. But what if I told you that the information you've been absorbing and digesting since you were born wasn't the full story?

What if there was another way to peacefully exist with food and your body no matter what they looked like? What if the picture of health is actually not just one picture but a group of many pictures? What if the things you're doing with your food and body are negatively affecting your kids both now and for the rest of their lives, and the impact of your actions could affect generations to come?

Before you start feeling guilt, shame, or fear, know that you're in good company. We are all navigating the same diet-filled messages around food and inaccurate pictures of health. Diet culture is the true culprit.

Author and anti-diet dietitian Christy Harrison defines diet culture as "a system of beliefs that worships thinness and equates it to health and moral value." While diet culture began as early as the 1800s, it grew exponentially from the 1920s forward, which means that we've all lived our entire lives under these false ideas around health, wellness, and body image. From the minute we were born, we were fed the message that thin is good and fat is bad. It's no wonder we don't know the "right" way to talk with our kids about food and body.

The most important thing to share is that it's never too late to learn a new way to approach your kids (and yourself) about these subjects. Creating a healthy relationship with food and body allows you and your kids the ability to focus time, energy and effort on the things that matter most in life—like making meaningful connections, finding and appreciating joy and pleasure, listening to and trusting your bodies, and being able to focus on the factors that actually do affect your health outside of body size. How you think and act around food and your body and what you say to your kids regarding their food and body all contribute to a solid foundation of trust, respect, compassion, and ultimately food freedom and body peace.

Traveling this path takes commitment and the ability to do some of your own soul searching, unlearning, and reflecting on how you grew up and your attitudes around food and body. But it can be done. As a mom of six, I was determined to help my kids avoid the same years of pain that I did around food and body, so I took a deep dive into healing my own relationship with both. For me this meant a certificate in nutrition, three health coach certifications, and a mentoring program with the top anti-diet coach in the nation. Everything I've learned, I'm sharing with you in this book.

What I know for sure is that the way you talk to (and model for) your kids about food and body matters. Mothers, in particular, play an incredibly influential role when it comes to food and body image. Not only are they often the ones buying, cooking, and preparing meals and snacks for their families, research shows that their families look to them for answers, ideas, thoughts, and beliefs around the topic of food and body. A study done by Harvard Medical School researchers found that "mothers who over-emphasize their concerns about body weight are significantly more likely to pass on these attitudes to their children" and that girls who simply thought their mothers wanted them to be thin were two to three times more likely to worry about losing weight.

Diet culture is keeping both you and your kids distracted with unattainable ideals instead of enjoying life and exploring your inner landscape. Girls as young as 7 to 9 years old have reported dieting, body dissatisfaction, and weight concerns, with a whopping 40% of school-age girls saying they've tried to lose weight (Journal of the Dietetic Association, Leann L. Birch, Ph.D., and Beth A. Abromovitz, MS). Another study (Flannery-Schroeder EC, Chrisler JC) showed that 22% of first-grade children shared they had dieted, while a study by A.M. Gustafson-Larson and R.D. Terry, found that 30% of third graders and 60% of sixth graders admitted they had dieted. Researchers have also now proven that children as young as 3 *years old* can develop body image issues. These numbers are downright staggering.

The truth is we live in a world steeped in diet culture, which means our kids are constantly bombarded both at home and school with messages about the thin ideal. Nutrition and physical activity are taught through the lens of weight "control" only, and kids remain uneducated about the truth around health and body size, the dangers of dieting, and the fact that diets don't work for the vast majority of people.

Did you know that research shows that more than 95% of people who attempt dieting will regain all the weight they've lost within 3 to 5 years (or sooner), and more than half of those people will gain back more weight than was initially lost? These findings beg the question —have we been taught the wrong way to think about bodies and health? Is there a better way?

The answer is unequivocally yes, and this book will show you the way to a better path. Regardless of your past, you can change your future. You can learn the truth about food and bodies, unlearn diet culture's false claims, grow, accept, evolve, and put yourself and your family on an anti-diet path. This path will not be straightforward. It will have twists and turns, valleys and mountain tops, but staying the course will forever change your life for the better.

My goal for you is to have *you and your kid* become "normal" eaters.

In her book *Normal Eating: Secrets of Feeding a Healthy Family,* Ellyn Satter defines normal eating as:

"Normal eating is going to the table hungry and eating until you are satisfied.

It is being able to choose the food you enjoy and eat it and truly get enough of it, not just stop eating because you think you should.

Normal eating is being able to give some thought to your food selection, so you get nutritious food, but not being so wary and restrictive that you miss out on enjoyable food.

Normal eating is giving yourself permission to eat sometimes because you are happy, sad, or bored, or just because it feels good.

Normal eating is mostly three meals a day, or four or five, or it can be choosing to munch along the way.

It is leaving some cookies on the plate because you know you can have some again tomorrow, or it is eating more now because they taste so wonderful.

Normal eating is overeating at times, feeling stuffed and uncomfortable. And it can be under eating at times and wishing you had more.

Normal eating is trusting your body to make up for your mistakes in eating.

Normal eating takes up some of your time and attention but keeps its place as only one important area of your life."

In short, normal eating is flexible. It varies in response to your hunger, your schedule, your proximity to food, and your feelings."

Normal eating means there's no right and wrong way to eat and enjoy your food. And normal bodies come in all different shapes, sizes, abilities, and colors. All bodies are good bodies. Just like you and I will never be "perfect" parents, achieving a "perfect" body is about as likely as my mom predicting Facebook and Instagram would be the place she could find out what her friends and family were doing 24/7 when she bought that loaf of whole wheat bread in the 1980s.

To help you on your path, I've divided this book up into sections with several tips listed within each section. At the end of each tip, you'll find a summary with what you need to know at a glance. Life is busy, and I know what it's like to want to get to the bold print so you know what to do right now! After each summary are a few short mantras you can reference to help you adopt a new attitude toward food and your body. At the end of the book, you will find some of my favorite resources as you begin or continue on your journey to helping yourself and your kid feel relaxed around food and accept their body.

Throughout the book, you'll be teaching yourself and your family the incredible importance of trusting natural instincts around food, feeling relaxed around eating, committing to self-compassion, and finding ways to manage stress and anxiety. The tools and tips you learn are going to be as much for you as they are for your kid. And learning is key. There's not one of us who's perfect when it comes to what we say and do around food and body, and that's okay and completely normal. You don't have to be perfect; you just need a commitment to ditching diets and raising anti-diet kids!

Even if you apply all the tips in this book, there's no arrival spot or finish line. I wish it were as easy as applying the book's concepts, and, *voila*, you will have arrived! Don't worry; you'll have the tools you need to stay above diet culture's waters and not get sucked back into the tumultuous diet culture sea. Diet culture's octopus tentacles will try to grab hold of you and pull you into a new diet-filled sea, but by the time you finish this book, you won't be tempted to go there or at least your temptations will be overcome by your confidence and commitment to your sanity and resolute promise to care for yourself as you'd care for your kid.

One final note that I would be remiss not to mention is that my voice is that of a white, cisgender, non-disabled, and straight-sized female. I recognize my incredible privileges because of my position. Throughout the book, I've tried to highlight some voices of those who are significantly marginalized and unfairly affected by fatphobia and diet culture's many ramifications, like those individuals who are in larger bodies, BIPOC, and/or LGBTQIA+.

I sincerely hope that this book is a resource and source of inspiration for you so that you can stop wasting your precious time, money, and energy on dieting and spend more time treasuring those you love and doing whatever your heart is calling you to do in this lifetime. You can be the one to break the diet cycle that may have been a part of your family's life for generations. This book is for my kids and all the kids who end up saving our lives in one way or another.

Introduction

I sat cradling our newborn baby. Swaddled tightly in her blanket, I felt like she was protected in my arms. I gazed at her perfection and covered her cheeks in kisses, sealing my vow to her that I would do everything in my power to keep her from experiencing a decades-long struggle with disordered eating and poor body image like I did. I was determined to break the cycle. And I imagine if you're reading this book, you are too.

Call them secrets, a roadmap, or tools—this book is full of the information, strategies, and suggestions around food and body I have gathered as I worked to keep that vow to not only my first child but the five who followed. Inside you'll find the compelling data and practical advice that helped me shift from worrying more about how to make organic baby food to instead considering how my lingering quirks around food and body were affecting my kids. You'll learn how to empower yourself and your kids around your food and bodies, and above all, you'll leave feeling *better*.

If you haven't had this aha moment yet, here it is: *Parenting is really a journey of self-discovery.* We think once we have our family, we'll become whole. Except, kids trigger us, challenge our patience, and take every ounce of energy we allow them to take. When we see our kids react or have experiences that were similar to our own childhood, it stirs up our own childhood experience. And therein lies the work.

On top of all that, we also must contend with living in a culture steeped in diet virtue, where the majority of people think fat is bad and thin is good. You and I grew up with those same USDA food pyramid posters plastered on our schools' walls. SnackWells filled our grocery store end caps, and Oprah pumped us up for her every new diet and weight loss success. I mean, if Oprah was doing it, we felt like we should at least be trying it, right? I'm guessing that, like me, you might have even subscribed to her daily 4 p.m. "church" and thought that surely the greatest talk show host of all time, with all the resources, knew what she was doing. Except, we know now that she didn't—and still doesn't—know the truth about dieting and weight loss, and as a generation we have tremendous room to grow when it comes to anti-diet knowledge.

It's not easy to choose an anti-diet path. We get bombarded with thousands of ads per day that tell us we should, can, and need to lose weight for better health and happiness. Diet culture has spread its sticky tentacles like an octopus into almost every aspect of our lives. We can't go to the doctor's office, school, or work; can't eat out at a restaurant; get on an airplane or go to an amusement park without seeing that people in larger bodies are considered less-than or discriminated against. We're constantly peppered with ads, images, movies, books, magazines, and social media posts that promote a culture of thinness and demote anybody living in a larger body.

Except that it's all a lie. Even if there was a safe way to permanently lose weight (there's not), research doesn't show that thin people are without disease. We're chasing an ideal that has no real benefit outside of the societal rightness our culture has placed on it.

There's no magic weight at which we can be guaranteed health, and yet every day hundreds of thousands of adults, teens, and kids convince themselves that life would be better if only they were thinner.

I was one of those kids. In my teenage years, I fell down what felt like a disordered eating rabbit hole. I didn't want to be there but also felt like I couldn't stop. (It made sense decades later when I realized that our behavior is strongly influenced by our biology, which was why it almost felt like it was happening to me instead of a choice I was making.) One week I was happily attending track practice after school, and the next week I was feeling self-conscious on my way to a track meet, picking the raisins out of my granola bar as a way to start having just a little bit less food. Fewer raisins turned into no more snacks, which turned into limiting food at meals or just skipping them altogether.

I felt ashamed and embarrassed since every other area of my life was together, like my family, school, dance, sports, and friends. My mom noticed the change in my eating habits and had me meet with my pediatrician and a nutritionist, and things slowly improved through high school. In college, I gained much-needed weight and started to shed my remaining restriction habits, but I still struggled with periodic binge eating episodes.

I kept wondering what was wrong with me and chided myself for being so weak in this one particular area of my life. How could a straight-A student not get something as basic as eating right? I wish I knew then that all of my "abnormal" behavior around food could be traced to one simple problem. I wasn't getting enough food. Period. Binge eating wasn't the problem; it was actually a sign that my body was trying to save me. I wasn't broken or addicted to carbs or needing more willpower. I didn't need to medicalize the very normal act of eating beyond fullness. I just needed to eat more food. I wish I had known then what I know now.

After a degree in exercise physiology in college and healing (for the most part) from my disordered ways, I spent years focused on what I thought was "health." I started working as a personal trainer and went on to run my own Pilates and yoga studio for a decade. I conveniently turned my disordered eating into a new obsession, orthorexia, which is an excessive preoccupation with eating healthy food. Gym rats were assumed to be "health" nuts, so I fit right in with no questions asked. Almonds for a snack? Good for you. Smoothie for breakfast? What's your recipe? All organic all the time? Count me in.

This worked for a while, until it didn't.

It wasn't until trying to conceive that I had to come face-to-face with peeling off those final layers of disordered patterns around food and finally learn to accept my body. Having kids wasn't just a passing fancy for me. It was something I had always wanted and dreamed about since I was a little girl. In some ways my kids literally helped save my life before I even met them because it was my drive to get pregnant that finally pushed me to truly heal.

When my husband and I were ready to start a family, I struggled with unexplained infertility for two years. I know this sounds strange to hear from a woman with six kids, but my road to parenthood had many twists and turns. This was the moment I felt like I had been waiting for since I was a little girl, and month after month, nothing was happening. I constantly wondered and worried about what could be wrong. In my mind I was the picture of health; I'd slayed those food demons long ago. I felt like I was throwing spaghetti at the wall trying this supplement or that acupuncturist or this fertility doctor, and I became depressed realizing that my dream might be out of reach.

About two years into my fertility journey, I met a nurse who gently suggested to me that maybe I just needed to gain a few pounds. I knew I could and needed to do more. I was willing to do literally anything, like that time I flew to New York to see the best acupuncturist in the city because, in my heart, I knew deep down that I wanted nothing more than to be a mom.

Not only did I gain weight, but I gained the knowledge I needed to understand why this all began and how to prevent this in the future. I had been so committed to "healthy" eating that I didn't think it could possibly be preventing me from getting what I most wanted. I started to realize that I needed to rethink my trips to Whole Foods and stop preventing myself from listening to my body's intuition around food and movement.

Fast forward to today. I now have a healthy relationship with both food and my body and am passionate about helping families foster an anti-diet lifestyle. Thanks in particular to my teacher and coach, Isabel Foxen Duke, and many other anti-diet crusaders that I will introduce you to throughout this book, I have learned so much that I want to share with you. As a certified Weight Neutral Coach™ and Diet Recovery Coach™ with the Center For Weight Neutral Coaching™ and a certified coach from The Life Coach School, I will be teaching you everything I know about how to best talk with your kids about food and their bodies.

What's most important though is that you examine your own relationship with food, your body, and diet culture. While this book was written with parents in mind, regardless of our role as caregivers, we are all humans deserving of peace. May you find some nugget of information within this book that helps you along your journey as both a human and a parent.

Section 1

Reprogramming Your Own Mind First

The Real Definition of Health

My son tore through his backpack like an archaeologist unearthing a fossil treasure. He plucked out a single sheet of paper and ran to me with it held high so no one could see or touch it before getting to me.

He presented the drawing, and I held it and smiled. "Wow! This is so cool," I cheered. "I love it!"

He beamed, his little body jumping up and down next to me in excitement. Suddenly he stopped and looked me square in the face.

"But do you think it's *good*, Mom?"

My heart sank a little as I absorbed his question and saw how his excitement was suddenly contingent on what I thought, not what he thought. Of course I wanted to say, "This is amazing, wonderful, great, fabulous!" Instead, I looked back at him and replied, "What do *you* think about your picture?"

"No, Mom, I want to know what *you* think," he pressed, a little annoyed.

"Tell me how you came up with this idea? Tell me more about the colors. Tell me how you got that cool shadow to make it look like it was moving?" I deflected.

He paused, holding out for his praise, and then relinquished, diving into a detailed explanation of the drawing at hand.

As anti-diet parents, it's our job to be a loving mirror for our kids when it comes to food and body. Just as I gently nudged my son back to his own internal process around the art, we can become guides for our kids, helping them focus inward instead of outward around food and body. The goal is to help them stop measuring their worth and value from outside opinions and instead focus on what feels good and right inside their own bodies.

Think about how many times your child has asked you if something was good or bad. It's natural for kids to look to their caregivers to gauge the world around them. As a kid, I too loved the yes, no, right, wrong, black or white answer. It was almost like I could take a deep breath and check one thing off an incredibly long and growing list of wonders about the world. Unfortunately, most of the answers to big, deep questions don't have a black and white answer, and the nuances of health are no different.

Our job is to help our children (and ourselves) understand that health isn't binary, and labeling other people's health as good or bad never captures the whole truth. Health is a continuum of choices and conditions, and we all live in the gray. We all have different physical abilities, too, which means my health definition is likely different from someone born with different abilities than me. Health is multidimensional and incorporates much more than how many times we've hit the gym or how many no-carb meals we've concocted.

Fat activist, comedian, triathlete, and writer Ragen Chastain reminds us, "Health is not a barometer of worthiness nor entirely within our control." We're sold the story that we can largely control our health through diet and exercise, but vegans get cancer and marathon runners have heart attacks. There's truly no golden ticket when it comes to health and wellness.

The World Health Organization defines health as "a state of

complete physical, mental, and social well-being, not merely the absence of disease." When thinking about how to help make health a practical concept for our kids, I would add that health is a state where you feel confident and comfortable in your skin. You have basic self-care and hygiene habits in place that you practice consistently. You treat your body with respect, appreciation, or at the very least, acceptance. You're not engaged in risky, life-threatening activities. You take good care of yourself by moving and eating in ways that feel good. You find ways to make and strengthen connections and seek support when you need help. While nobody can predict or control the future, you're making a reasonable effort to ensure that you have a long, happy life. That's health.

What are the real factors that contribute to health? Instead of thinking of health as good or bad behaviors, what really matters?

Research shows that these factors have a major influence on our health:

1. Exercise. Specifically, physical activity that averages 12 times per month.
2. Five servings of fruits and vegetables per day. (This doesn't mean you need to eat enormous salads at every meal.)
3. No more than one alcoholic drink per day for women and two drinks per day for men.
4. No smoking.
5. Adequate sleep. Six to 8 hours per night.
6. Stress levels do matter. Your health improves if you can lead a life with low-to-moderate stress levels. When stressful events arise, you have tools (breathing, meditation, family or friend support, yoga, etc.) to settle your nervous system and bring your stress levels back down.

7. The amount of autonomy you have at your job. The higher up you are in your job, the better your health outcomes.
8. The social connections you have with others.
9. Genetics.
10. Environmental factors like pollution.

Notice that "weight" is not on that list anywhere. We'll talk more about that in the next section, but it bears mentioning now as you begin to broaden your definition of health. Health happens along a spectrum—a plethora of conditions, factors, genetic predispositions, and choices. Health is not only defined or determined by weight or body size.

* * *

SUMMARY

Body shape and size don't determine our health or value. From the minute we enter the world we're taught that size is paramount in our overall health. In reality, true health is actually determined by many factors, like our environment, socioeconomic status, and our genetics, which are largely out of our control. Health isn't binary, as in you have health or you don't have health. Instead, health happens across a spectrum and adopting the attitude of living in the gray when it comes to health versus a black or white mentality is an important step on your food peace journey. Getting enough sleep, not smoking, decreasing stress, limiting alcohol intake, choosing a career with autonomy, moving your body, and eating some fruits and veggies are all things you can control and that can actually improve your health.

* * *

Mantra

- True health isn't determined by my body shape or size.
- There are many things outside of body size that I can control that can have a positive impact on my health. There are many ways to be healthy.
- Feeling good comes from my internal wisdom and isn't based on what other people deem as the "right" ways to move or eat.
- Health isn't entirely in my control nor a measure of my worthiness.

The Weight Myth

I eagerly stood leaning over the edge of the metal fence with my sign in hand, scanning the massive crowd of runners for my husband. My eyes tried to focus on the blue shirt he told me he'd be wearing, but it felt nearly impossible with so many bodies rushing by in a flash. My adrenaline was already pumping, as my friend and I had to walk, ride the T, and shimmy our way to a good vantage point during Boston's Marathon Monday, and I felt my hands getting sweaty as I worried that I'd missed my chance to cheer him on at mile 14.

While I eagerly waited to spot my husband, I began to realize I was seeing runners of just about every age, body size, and ability. Short, tall, fat, thin, medium, wheelchairs, artificial limbs, and guides for the blind were all represented. Pink tutus, crazy wigs, and barefoot bravehearts dotted the running crowd. I stood there in awe, feeling inspired by the variety of runners, and I found myself vowing to run my own marathon someday. Being able to see stereotypes about people of various sizes blown up in the best possible way in front of my eyes was a very powerful experience. I realized people are really capable of anything, despite popular limiting beliefs.

Truly, when it comes to being healthy, for 90% of people, weight just doesn't matter that much. Research shows that a difference of 5, 10, 15, 20, 40, or more pounds is not going to make one significantly healthier or extend their lifespan. A person really can be fat and fit (yet there's no obligation to be "fit" if that's not something they value or want to make a priority). If we really want to be healthier, we need to focus on the factors listed in the previous section, not on weight.

When you go to the doctor, the markers that can give you an indication about your health outside of the number on the scale are blood cholesterol, blood pressure, blood sugar, complete blood count and metabolic panel, thyroid levels, iron, and B12. Ask your doctor to use those measures as a starting point to discuss your health instead of looking at your weight alone.

There's one exception when weight matters. If a person's weight falls into the "extremely low" or "extremely high" category, then yes, weight does impact health. For instance, if a person is extremely underweight (starving to death) or in the final 4% of the weight bell curve, their weight can adversely affect their health. However, if a person falls in the middle of the weight bell curve (as the vast majority of people do) and not at the extreme low end or high end, their weight doesn't impact their health much at all.

One of the most pivotal moments in my life was discovering the book *Health At Every Size (HAES): The Surprising Truth About Your Weight*, written by Lindo Bacon, Ph.D. Bacon, a weight science researcher and associate nutritionist at the University of California, says:

"Health At Every Size is the new peace movement. It is an inclusive movement, recognizing that our social characteristics, such as our size, race, national origin, sexuality, gender, disability status, and other attributes, are assets and acknowledges and challenges the structural and systemic forces that impinge on living well. It also supports people of all sizes in adopting healthy behaviors."

The Health At Every Size framework started from a group of fat activists and healthcare providers in the 1990s who believed that people of all sizes could pursue health-promoting behaviors without focusing on weight loss or dieting in any way. While Bacon's book is an influential text in the HAES space, there's debate and concern about promoting the HAES movement by white, straight-sized individuals without lived experience in larger bodies. (Bacon is straight bodied.) Another voice who has emerged as an authority is Nancy Ellis-Ordway, a psychotherapist of 30 years with lived experience in a larger body. Her book, *Thrive at Any Weight: Eating to Nourish Body, Soul, and Self-Esteem,* is another incredibly powerful book for anyone wanting to learn more about HAES.

The HAES movement and the research around it have helped shine a light on the importance of adopting health behaviors without the goal of weight loss. In the past 15 years, several studies have investigated the impact of HAES programs on various health and well-being indicators. Two systematic reviews (Bacon & Aphramor, 2011; Clifford et al., 2015) and a subsequent randomized-controlled trial (Mensinger, Calogero, & Tylka, 2016) demonstrated that the HAES approach was more effective in improving various aspects of physiological, psychological, and behavioral factors than usual care or alternative treatment options.

If weight isn't the contributing factor for health as many of us assume, then what can explain the negative health outcomes that people in larger bodies often experience? In response, researchers have been asking the question: *"Could weight stigma be a much larger problem than weight itself?"* Weight stigma refers to the oppression and unfair treatment of larger-bodied people, which makes it extremely difficult for them to get equal employment, access to healthcare that's effective and non-discriminatory, and other basic human rights that we all deserve.

A 2017 study (content warning: weight-stigmatizing language, BMI numbers) found that regardless of their actual weight, people who experienced higher levels of weight stigma had more than twice the risk of high allostatic load—a measure of cumulative stress on all body systems that puts people at greater risk of type 2 diabetes, cardiovascular disease, and mortality. Other studies have also shown that HAES curricula at the school and university levels led to improved body image, self-esteem, and eating attitudes in children (Kater, Rohwer, & Londre, 2002; Niide, Davis, Tse, & Harrigan, 2013); intuitive eating, body esteem, anti-fat attitudes, and dieting behaviors in university students (Humphrey, Clifford, & Morris, 2015); and knowledge, attitudes, beliefs, and skills in teachers (Shelley, O'Hara, & Gregg, 2010). Imagine the impact of kids having this potent messaging earlier in life.

If you've ever been one of those people who thought they needed to lose weight "to get healthier," I encourage you to check out the HAES website, which is filled with great information, including how to find an HAES provider in your area: https://haescommunity.com/. I also recommend the work of Ragen Chastain. Both her blog, Dances With Fat, and the HAES health sheets she co-authored with Dr. Louise Metz provide thorough explanations for a variety of health conditions, like heart disease, diabetes, high blood pressure, high cholesterol, joint pain, and PCOS; how weight stigma plays a role; and how you can talk with your doctor to receive vital weight-neutral care. Ragen brilliantly says:

> "Health is not an obligation or barometer of worthiness. Health is affected by many factors that are often out of our control. Activism around improving health must center on issues of social justice and access."

But what about all your dieting friends and family? How do you get or stay on an anti-diet path when your closest connections are weight obsessed?

Remember the reality show *The Biggest Loser*? It was hard not to get sucked into that train wreck of a show, but even harder to admit that we all watched as contestants were literally being starved and tortured before our eyes for our "entertainment." The thing is, many of the contestants have come forward, especially Kai Hibbard, who wrote a book detailing her negative experience on the show, talking about the adverse health effects they underwent in order to "succeed." Follow-up studies done on *The Biggest Loser* contestants show that their metabolisms never went back to "normal" after participating in such dramatic weight loss. And yet as a society, we're obsessed with their transformations, regardless of the reality of the health outcome.

Have you been asked by friends, family, or coworkers to participate in a biggest loser challenge and been tempted to join their efforts? You've likely thought you should try because, if the people on TV can have such dramatic results, why can't you do it, too?

If you're feeling pressured to join a weight loss challenge, try this script:

"It's great that you want to be healthier. I love you, and I want you to have a long, happy life! But if you're serious about getting healthier, you might want to focus on things like sleep, exercise, and cutting back on alcohol much more than you focus on weight. Because those factors actually make a much bigger difference than your weight does."

Or you can simply say:

"Diets have never worked for me and they feel like a waste of time so I'm not interested."

Remember that over 95% of people who attempt weight loss will gain back the weight lost in 3-5 years, and about 65% of those people will gain back more weight than they initially lost.

Not only are weight loss studies typically poorly done (footnote 2), much of the weight loss success stories are lost to attrition but still counted as a "success." One of the most famous studies, *Medicare's Search for Effective Obesity Treatments: Diets Are Not the Answer,* conducted by Traci Mann, A. Janet Tomiyama, Erika Westling, Ann Marie Lew, Barbra Samuels, and Jason Chatman (link goes to article) (footnote 3) shows how ineffective dieting really is for the vast majority of people.

Here is an excerpt of the study findings:

"You can initially lose 5 to 10 percent of your weight on any number of diets, but then the weight comes back. We found that the majority of people regained all the weight, plus more. Sustained weight loss was found only in a small minority of participants, while complete weight regain was found in the majority. Diets do not lead to sustained weight loss or health benefits for the majority of people. In addition, the studies do not provide consistent evidence that dieting results in significant health improvements, regardless of weight change. In sum, there is little support for the notion that diets lead to lasting weight loss or health benefits."

Still not convinced? A panel of experts convened by the National Institutes of Health determined that "In controlled settings, participants who remain in weight loss programs usually lose approximately 10% of their weight. However, one-third to two-thirds of the weight is regained within one year [after weight loss], and almost all is regained within five years."

Don't succumb to changing your body to fit into oppressive beauty standards. Instead, work on changing the way you view your own health and body. Challenge your own fatphobic thoughts and your judgment about other people of various sizes, both thin and fat.

Writer Virginia Sole-Smith, the author of *The Eating Instinct, Food Culture, Body Image, and Guilt in America*, reminds us that "In a 2012 analysis of almost 12,000 adults, researchers found that lifestyle habits were a better predictor of mortality than body mass index (BMI) because regardless of their weight class, people lived longer when they practiced healthy habits like not smoking, drinking alcohol in moderation, eating five or more servings of fruits and vegetables daily and exercising 12 or more times per month."

One conversation at a time, starting in our own homes, we can re-educate people, especially our kids, about what "health" actually means. Because it really has almost nothing to do with the number on the scale or your clothing size.

* * *

SUMMARY

Although weight and health seem inextricably connected, weight alone isn't as large a determinant of health as we think. In fact, body size simply isn't a meaningful contribution to health. If we can rewrite our brains and our kids' brains to understand this deep truth, then we're very likely to seek health behaviors for the sake of health alone and not to manipulate our body size. Practicing acceptance of our own body size and having gratitude for our size can help remove weight stigma toward ourselves and others, which has a greater impact on health than weight alone. There are some incredible resources from Ragen Chastain and Dr. Louise Metz listed above that will help you advocate for weight-neutral care if you have a health condition that's linked with weight. Let's redefine health for ourselves and teach our kids the truth about health and weight. Your success and happiness can never be determined by your pant size.

* * *

MANTRA

- I can be proud of my size without feeling shame about my size because size and health aren't equal.
- My size doesn't determine my health.
- Virtually everyone who loses weight will regain all if not more of their weight lost. Do I really want to spend my time and energy with this kind of return on investment (ROI)?

Ditch Diets for Good

There's a board game my sons love to play that drives me mad. It's called Sum Swamp, and in the game each player has to enter an area called the endless loop. Once you're in the loop, you have to roll the exact number on the dice that matches the number of squares that will land you on the exit square. If you don't roll the magic number, you keep going around and around and around the loop. It's maddening.

Playing this game always takes me back to all the time I wasted on the diet/binge loop. There's the promise of the win (weight loss and health) if you follow "the rules." (Paleo! Vegan! Low carb! No fat! High fat! Gluten-free! Sugar-free! Intermittent fasting!) Everything seems to work initially, and you feel lucky. But at some point, your diet "skills" stop working, the dieter's high wears off, and you're going in circles realizing you've regained the weight you initially lost. What they didn't tell you when you started the diet game is that 95% will regain their weight lost and two-thirds of dieters not only regain their initial weight lost but actually gain additional weight. It's a no-win circle.

You're not alone. According to a study by *SELF* magazine and eating disorder researcher Cynthia Bulik, three out of four women aged 25 to 45 eat, think, and behave abnormally around food. Some women in the survey considered themselves career dieters, others were secret eaters binging on foods in private, others were calorie prisoners terrified to gain weight, and some participated in purging activities while some resorted to extreme exercise.

As I write this book, the diet industry rakes in $72 billion a year as people keep going around and around the diet-cycling loop. Meanwhile our suffering and the suffering of our children is fueling profits for big pharmaceuticals, doctors, and surgeons, countless self-proclaimed diet gurus, the food industry, commercial diet center chains, medical weight loss programs, and more. Virtually no diet works in the long run, so the industry knows you have to keep dieting. No other industry gets away with such a high return on a failed product. No medication would get approval by the FDA at the rate that diets fail.

All this said, there are no easy solutions when we live in a fatphobic world. Who doesn't want what thin privilege has to offer? Better healthcare, more job opportunities, the ability to shop for clothing in stores, shame- and stigma-free interactions with family and doctors, and the (false) promise of love and self-worth. So we roll the dice again and again.

As parents we have a powerful position to begin change within our own homes, but first we have to change our own minds. When we look at the health facts around dieting versus the vanity insanity that diet culture wants to distract us with, we see that there's clear evidence that dieting is physically and emotionally harmful. In fact, it's actually weight-related shame and stigma that lead to stress-related diseases like heart disease. Some studies show that weight stigma can account for most if not all of the negative health outcomes people in larger bodies experience. Maybe it isn't the weight itself that's the cause of negative health outcomes after all. Weight might be a correlating factor, but not the causing factor as most people assume and have been told by our healthcare system.

Weight cycling, also known as "yo-yo dieting," is another common health risk factor among higher-weight people (and others across the weight spectrum). Like weight stigma, weight cycling has negative mental and physical health effects independent of BMI. It's associated with a higher risk of binge eating, high blood pressure, cardiovascular disease, and mortality, among other things. In fact, studies have found weight cycling may explain all of the excess heart risk seen in people in higher BMI categories. (footnote 4)

If we can reprogram ourselves to understand that it's a rigged game, we might not be so tempted to play and get stuck in an endless losing loop. Even the 2 to 5% of "successful" dieters show signs of physical and emotional duress similar to those with active eating disorders. And for what?

Even though our world favors a thin body, how much of our lives are we willing to waste on a system that not only doesn't work but also ignores the fact that health is completely possible in a larger body? Real health has nothing to do with a number on the scale or our clothing size.

There's not any type of diet that's worth your time, sanity, health, money, or energy. When you get off the endless loop of dieting and get back to the real game of life, you come home to your joy and your real self. The real you that goes about your days not obsessing about food or your body—who can make real and deep connections (the amount of chatter that dieting consumes your brain with is real and significant) with people who matter in your life. You really don't have to diet to feel like you're winning at life.

For everyone, this will look differently. Maybe getting off the loop looks like putting down your measuring cups and giving yourself full allowance of all foods and bringing back some joy and pleasure into your meals. Maybe it means you stop following diet or weight loss promoting people or companies. Maybe it means you stop reading food and ingredient labels with the intensity of an undercover investigator. Maybe it means just generally relaxing around food. As you adjust your habits, look to your kids for inspiration, especially young kids. They were born intuitive eaters and only adjust their habits as diet culture sinks in.

I want to leave you with this definition of diet culture from author, podcaster, and anti-diet dietitian Christy Harrison because quitting dieting might be one of the hardest things you'll do. Your brain will likely seek some sort of control around food, and it's important to awaken your awareness the next time someone is trying to convince you of the latest and greatest way to change your body. If any "plan," "protocol," or "reset" you're considering contains any of these characteristics, please run the opposite direction as fast as Usain Bolt can run the 100-meter dash. The word diet has become a bit of a four-letter word, so diet marketers are cleverly shapeshifting and morphing into "wellness" and "lifestyle" plans. But buyer beware, a diet is still a diet if it tells you what to eat, how much to eat, and when to eat.

"Diet culture is a system of beliefs that:

1. Worships thinness, muscularity, and particular body shapes, and equates these things to health and moral virtue.

2. Promotes weight loss and body reshaping as means of attaining higher status.

3. Demonizes certain foods, food components, food groups, and styles of eating while elevating others."

If you need more convincing that diets don't work, Christy's book, *Anti-Diet: Reclaim Your Time, Money, Well-Being and Happiness Through Intuitive Eating,* is my most recommended anti-diet book for helping people understand diet history, the dangers of diets, why diets don't promote health, and so much more. Linda Bacon's *Health At*

Every Size is a close second. These books will help you better question the upheld idea that thin is good and fat is bad and realize that any weight loss is almost always fleeting and that yo-yo dieting alone can put you at greater health risk than if you would've stayed at the same (even if it is a larger body) size.

Lastly, and most importantly, you must be willing to let go of your pursuit of thinness and not conflate your pursuit of health with your pursuit of thinness. Check your motivations behind any of your habits around food and be honest if any of your motivations are rooted in weight.

* * *

Summary

Diets don't work. Period. There's not a single study that shows long-term success (sustained weight loss for greater than 5 years) for any diet. Over 95% of people who diet will regain their weight in 5 years (or sooner) and two-thirds of those dieters will gain more weight than they initially lost. The bottom line is that endorsing any kind of diet for yourself or your child is detrimental both physically and mentally in both the short and long term. Dieting typically results in what I refer to as the endless loop where you lose weight, regain the weight, blame yourself (the diet could never be to blame), and try the next best promise in weight loss. You continue going round and round the vicious circle of weight loss followed by weight gain (yo-yo dieting), which is dangerous for your health. Ditching diets is perhaps the clearest and easiest anti-diet rule to understand, but one of the hardest to follow, especially if you've spent any amount of time dieting. The weight-loss-promising formulas come lurking in many cloaks. Most recently, the "wellness" or "lifestyle" gurus try to convince you that they're anti-diet when they're anything but anti-diet. We'll talk more about ways to channel your dieting anxiety because using food as a means to find control is a very real strategy that many become accustomed to, but this strategy doesn't produce lasting results. Steer clear of ANYTHING that tells you what to eat, when to eat, or how much to eat.

* * *

MANTRA

- Diets only work for a tiny fraction of people, basically unicorns.
- I'm not willing to waste my time, money, sanity, or energy on a system designed to fail.
- My body isn't the problem; diet culture is the problem.

Intuitive Eating Principles

If dieting is bad, how are we supposed to be eating? And how can we support ourselves with food for long-term health? Dietitians Evelyn Tribole and Elyse Resch sought to answer these questions in the early 1990s. Knowing that 95 to 97% of dieters fail, these two women got together in hopes of helping dieters be the successful 3 to 5% of people who could maintain their 30-pound weight loss for more than 5 years. They created beautiful meal plans and strategies that worked in the short term, but their clients would inevitably need their help once the weight came back. They knew there had to be a better way, and intuitive eating was born.

In 1995 they compiled their findings into their first book, *Intuitive Eating,* and shared their 10 Principles of Intuitive Eating. (A note: If you choose to buy the book/workbook, make sure to get the fourth edition, as earlier editions have some diet speak woven into the material.) Early on, intuitive eating was often used as a way to maintain or lose weight. That's not the intention these days, and we'll explore a few of the principles through the lens of *not* turning intuitive eating into another diet. With that said, mastering intuitive eating isn't necessary on an anti-diet journey, but it can be helpful for approaching your relationship with food from a new vantage point. As always, take what resonates and works for you.

Reject Dieting in All Forms

I clearly remember the day I finally gave up dieting. I was a few weeks into a new "eating plan" (ahem, diet) endorsed by the founder of a life coach school where I was certified, and I had been surviving on peanut butter rice cakes and salad. My list of "allowed" foods was less than 20 items, maybe even 10, if I was being realistic. I had been following the "plan" perfectly, which meant that I "shouldn't" be hungry. Except I was hungry. Majorly hungry. I literally felt like I had to sit on my hands, chew gum, or slug sparkling water to quell my growling stomach between my paltry meals.

One day I was sharing with my husband the list of all the things that were off-limits, and he paused and looked at me. "Wow, that really doesn't leave much for you to eat," he said as he laughed nervously.

For some reason, his comment, coupled with the fact that I was constantly hungry and trying to talk myself out of eating snacks, led me to throw up the white flag...for good. I was done with a capital D. I vividly remember thinking that if this was what it was going to take to "live longer" or be "healthier" for the rest of my life, it just wasn't worth my time and energy anymore. I was done doing the so-called virtuous deeds to live a long life. My wellness habit was feeling a lot more like punishment and self-abuse than a way to prolong my life.

In that moment I was finally taking the first—and most important —step of intuitive eating (and any anti-diet journey). I was rejecting dieting in all forms and adopting full allowance around all foods.

It's important to note that this includes both physical *and* emotional forms of restriction. Emotional restriction is so often over-looked, yet it is equally damaging as physical restriction. Physical dieting or restriction is following a plan like Paleo, Whole 30, Inter-mittent Fasting, or Weight Watchers (WW) with the intent of restricting the amount of food you eat in order to manipulate your body size. Emotional restriction or dieting is prompted by the voice in your head that tells you what to eat and not eat, "punishes" you verbally, or shames you for your actions around food. The blame and guilt you feel after hearing this voice can lead you to alter (both decrease or increase) the amount of food you eat because you feel wrong or bad for choosing a certain food. These two types of restric-tion very often exist together, and emotional restriction can linger well after you've stopped physically restricting your food intake.

Both physical and emotional restrictions are dangerous and don't work for 95 to 98% of people. Let that statistic really sink in. You'll hear it mentioned time and again in these pages because it's an impor-tant dieting fact worth repeating. Literally only a tiny fraction of dieters, we're talking unicorns, are succeeding, and even the "success-ful" ones show signs consistent with chronic disordered eaters. There is no long-term scientific study that demonstrates safe, effective, or long-lasting means to weight loss. Even the slightest bit of restriction, what you might not even consider "real" dieting because it's minimal, is felt within the body and mind. While this is a very hard truth to swallow, it's necessary to understand that any failed attempts at dieting aren't your fault but are instead due to a faulty system that has cleverly blamed your shortcomings, like strength, intelligence, and willpower, as the reasons for your failure. To stop dieting is not only difficult if you've been a lifelong dieter, but it's necessary in order to repair your relationship with your body and food.

A little more on physical restriction:

Not only is dieting a predictor of weight gain, but dieting will trigger the body to gain more body fat as a means to survive. When you physically restrict, your cells don't know that you are cutting back on calories as part of a weight loss plan. They think you're starving, and there's not enough food (which sadly is a reality for many people around the world). Dieting can also lead to your body breaking down your muscle and lean tissue for energy. Additionally, dieting lowers your leptin levels, which is a hormone that helps trigger feelings of fullness. Without the proper hunger and fullness hormone levels, you're likely to feel like you need forks in both fists at mealtime to achieve satiation, and nobody will be able to pry you away from the table until you've had enough food. Your body doesn't know when the next food or meal will come, so it's incredibly smart at adding fat reserves to the body to utilize during any future famine, real or self-imposed.

What about all the plans and protocols that claim to be custom for you? All those diets that have the magic ingredient or the one loophole, or that thing that's been missing from all the other diets that make them, and you, *verrrry* special?

It's virtually impossible for any diet to be customized to your individual hunger levels or be based around foods that will be magically satisfying and pleasurable for you, not to mention include foods that are culturally important to you and your family. There's no magic, and I promise you there's no loophole that's yet to be discovered. Constant exposure to external recommendations about diets and nutrition information comes at a price. Constantly checking food for calories, fat and fiber grams, and sugars gives us a sense that we can't be trusted and focuses on an external versus an internal experience around food and our bodies. If you think someone else knows better than your own body, you'll very likely make choices from a place of fear and anxiety and rely less and less on your body's cues. Your body is ultimately wise and has all the answers you need to know around food built into its extraordinarily advanced internal system of food satiation and satiety network. The most intricate Apple computer doesn't come close to your body's multifaceted system that drives and controls your energetic needs.

Think about when you were a kid; you made perfect intuitive choices around food. Then at some point, you decided you needed to depend on diet books, diet gurus, influencers, and the latest issue of *Health Magazine* because you knew that being thinner was better. I encourage you to let go of health blogs, nutrition articles, and external diets as you start the intuitive eating process. If you need inspiration, simply watch young kids around food. They approach eating with a sense of zest and playfulness that we lose over time thanks to diet culture's messaging that fat is bad and thin is good.

A little more on emotional restriction:

The voice in your head constantly telling you what you should, shouldn't, can't, won't, or not eat is what you want to begin paying attention to and learning from. Next time you notice yourself enjoying a delicious meal and start talking yourself out of getting a second helping or having dessert, please recognize this as a form of emotional restriction. Whenever you hear this voice, the best thing to do is ask yourself, "Why?"

Why am I preventing myself from having what I want? Am I worried about what others will think? Am I worried that I won't be able to stop? Am I worried that I'll gain weight? Is there something else stressful going on in my life that my mind is coming back to controlling food as a way to ease anxiety? It might even help to talk to yourself in the first person. "Sarah, you can eat whatever you want. You're a grown woman who can trust her body's needs."

Once you can answer the why behind your actions, you can remind yourself that your job is to let your body's instincts around food take over. You'll be able to feel like you can stop with the constant worries about this food, that ingredient, or this food plan. The goal is to be able to have the attitude that food is just food. Practice saying to yourself: "It's just food, and I can relax around whatever decision I make around food based on what my body is telling me to do! I don't need to diet for safety, control, or status." As my mentor Isabel Foxen Duke says, "My food is going to be what it's going to be."

Get in the habit of reminding yourself that there's no right or wrong way to act around food and there are no rules around food. Whenever you hear this little voice in your head, call it out and say, *"Oh, hi! It's you again. You're that voice that pops up when I'm feeling anxious or worried about my life or my food or my body. I wonder what you're trying to tell me today. I'm not going to let you keep me in dieters' prison, but I will listen to you and learn how I can support you and your needs both when it comes to food and outside of food."* As a compassionate observer, you can take note without prescribing any shame or blame, or guilt. Being able to let go of the diet voice (or learn how to talk to it or override it depending on the situation) is key to allowing yourself to hear the messaging from your innate internal voice that's perfectly programmed to your body's needs. While this voice might not disappear completely, your ability to recognize it and not respond by physically restricting yourself is the goal. Discovering, allowing, and respecting your intuitive voice is a crucial step to finding peace and freedom around food.

* * *

SUMMARY

Both physical restriction (eating less food) and emotional restriction (altering your food intake based on what the dieting voice inside your head tells you you can and can't do) are considered forms of dieting. Your goal is to be able to recognize both forms of restriction and become a compassionate observer who asks, "What is it that I need right now?" Remind yourself that physically or emotionally restricting your food is never the answer. Other questions to ask yourself might be:

Am I feeling worried or anxious somewhere else in my life? Are my fears about weight gain and what others think of me taking over my body's desire for more food? How can I trust my instincts around food and let go of the thoughts that try dictating what I should and shouldn't do around food?

Your goal is to get to the place where you think food is just food and that your instincts around food are normal and natural and meant to be honored.

* * *

MANTRA

- I reject any and all forms of dieting.
- I can allow myself to eat the food I want without feeling any guilt or shame.
- If I'm feeling anxious about food, I'll get curious about where else in my life I might be feeling anxious and focus my energy on solving those anxieties versus using food control, aka dieting, as a coping strategy.

Honor Your Hunger

With six kids, I love finding new adventures and places to explore. One of the first things I think about before we venture out on a novel day is not necessarily if everyone will have fun, if the drive is too long, if I have enough entertainment plus digital devices, or if we'll have enough food (I always pack more than we need). Nope, it's really all about the bathroom. Will there be any bathrooms and where are they?

You know why?

Because someone ALWAYS has to go in our big family. I loved going to the bathroom while pregnant because people took one look at me and literally parted the Red Sea to make a path to the nearest stall. Nobody argues with the prego mama, and nobody argues with that unmistakable toddler potty dance. Nobody tried to convince me I didn't have to go. It's a nonnegotiable, needs-to-happen-now kind of thing. You very likely were reminded when you potty trained your kid that you just don't mess with Mother Nature.

You probably don't think about food and hunger the same as your urge to use the bathroom, but both are biological functions that are largely outside of our control. We have cells, hormones, memories, and chemical messengers that combine together to let us know exactly what we need and when in order to not only survive but thrive. I want you to consider what it would be like for you to allow your hunger sensations to arise and not argue, dampen, deter, ignore, or negotiate with them. No extra glass of water, no chewing gum, no zero sugar beverage, no carbonated bubbly drink to wash those hunger signals away. Simply recognize them and respond with no additional story or drama. I had to pee, so I went to the bathroom. I was hungry, so I ate. It's really that simple. The details of what you ate really aren't that important in the grand scheme of things; it mostly matters that you ate until satisfaction, even if that meant getting full or eating more than you normally would at a given meal or snack.

Dieters often view fullness as a problem or that something has gone wrong. For a dieter, fullness can be a sign of failure or weakness, while hunger is a sign that you're "doing it right" or a signal that can and should be ignored. While a dieter often feels guilt and shame about fullness, they celebrate hunger as a sign of success and actually end up amplifying hunger by tricking their body with drinking water or eating "air foods" like rice cakes to appease any original important hunger messages. Have you ever said to yourself, "Yessss! I made myself wait long enough to feel those hunger pains. I must be melting the fat away now!!!" This is diet culture's messaging that wants us to believe that not listening to and disconnecting from our bodies is the right and noble thing to do. Trying to become smaller has somehow become a side hustle or even a full-time job for many women.

I give you full permission to drop this duty to ignore your hunger. I want to encourage you instead to honor your hunger and see if you not only feel better mentally and physically but also notice a deeper, more honest relationship with your body. Honoring is a two-part process. We first *listen* to our body's hunger cues and then we *respond* to those cues with food. Over time we learn to retrust our body, and our body learns to retrust us. Yes, I will feed you when you give me the cues that you're hungry. Yes, I will eat until you feel satiated and satisfied.

Sometimes we tell ourselves that we should stop eating because we are satiated or have that belly-full feeling, but we don't actually feel satisfied. Becoming an intuitive eater means that you honor your satisfaction, too, and that you eat until you are both full *and* satisfied. That might look like eating just a little bit or it might look like eating past the point of fullness because it feels like what your body wants and needs. Think about when you've had a delicious dinner, and your belly is content, but a piece of chocolate or a scoop of ice cream would be really satisfying and hit the spot.

You might be wondering what to eat if you've lost communication with your body. Similar to having your phone on airplane mode where the signal is lost, dieters very often lose communication with their bodies as a way to get through the demanding and untenable diet requirements.

Here are two ways to get you back in touch with your innate hunger cues:

1. At the very minimum, you should be eating (and preparing for your family) three full meals a day that contain a variety of food groups (fat, protein, carbohydrate, and bonus points for fiber). That doesn't mean your meal looks like crackers and cheese or yogurt. Those are snacks, which I encourage you to have morning, afternoon, and evening as desired, too! Having enough energy throughout the day is very important and can only be achieved when you eat from a variety of food groups and enough of those foods.

2. In order to get back in touch with your innate hunger cues, I encourage you to eat every 3 to 4 hours. If you've lost

touch with your hunger sensations after years of deprivation, eating on a more regular schedule will give you dependable hunger signals. It's also important to know that hunger can be experienced differently by people. Hunger can show up as physical sensations and cues that might be felt in the stomach, like rumbling or emptiness, in the head in the form of light-headedness or a headache, or in the throat. Some may even feel shaky or weak. You can also get emotional signals like irritability, fatigue, or overall lethargy and notice an increase in your thoughts about food and eating. If you're thinking about food, chances are your body is letting you know it's going to be time to refuel very soon. You might think that true hunger only happens when your stomach is growling, but that's very often a sign that you're well past your regular hunger cues and have entered a "feed me now!" zone of hunger.

What if you think you or your kid's hunger cues are signaling too much, like the text notifications on your teenager's phone? If you're hungry an hour after you just ate, it's okay. You or your kid may have had a higher volume of exercise the day before, are recovering from an illness or injury, or be experiencing a growth spurt, and the body is simply catching up on the calories it needs. Whatever you ate initially wasn't enough to satiate your body, and there's no need to argue with your body's hunger cues. It could also be hormonal changes, or you or your kid are just having a hungrier day. Regardless, we respond to biological hunger cues as a signal to our body that we are listening, responding, and building trust. No problem, no drama.

Just like you prioritize and pay attention to other body cues like thirst, your level of fatigue, your stress levels, or when you have to go to the bathroom, you can and should prioritize your hunger. Hunger falls into the category of taking care of your physical and emotional needs and must happen every day in order to maximize your health. Besides making sure you have enough to eat, other things you can do to prioritize your health include getting enough sleep, having healthy relationships, moving your body, and living in a safe environment. Our hunger cues work best when we are well-rested, hydrated, and don't have high levels of stress. Trust your body, and don't let your brain get in the way with arguing, convincing, tricking, and cajoling. If you're hungry, eat. It's also important to remind yourself that you can eat again whenever you're hungry. It's also good to remind yourself that you don't need to worry about what your food might look like tomorrow. If you only had today, how would you choose to eat?

I purposely avoid talking about numbers in this book, but it's important to understand that the often quoted 2,000 calories a day for the average woman is not enough energy intake. This governmental standard is based on self-reported information, which is often 20 to 30% incorrect because reporters usually underestimate their intake. Women who've dieted with the government recommendation, or even fewer calories, very often lose a menstrual cycle or show other signs of restriction, like temperature regulation problems, hair loss, brittle nails, dull skin, or fatigue. Most women usually need 2,500 to 3,500 calories at a minimum. The higher end is recommended for women under 25 or women who have high levels of activity (think women with young children, which means unavoidable amounts of energy expenditure). Those recovering from disordered eating very often need more than 3,500 calories per day so the body has enough energy to deal with the backlog of cell and tissue repair and to return the neuroendocrine and metabolic systems back to normal.

Anytime you start thinking about food (remember, hunger is not defined by physical sensations alone), make a commitment to eat within 20 minutes of this thought. The dieting mind will make all sorts of excuses not to eat, like, "I shouldn't be hungry now," "It's not time to eat," "It's not convenient to stop for food," "The food available isn't going to be 'healthy' enough," etc. Plan ahead for this by having a variety of snacks available while you're on the go so you can adequately respond to your body's hunger cues.

* * *

SUMMARY

We've been taught that fullness is a sign of weakness or wrong, and hunger is a sign of strength or a signal that can be manipulated or ignored. Contrary to diet culture's beliefs, hunger is a sensation that is biological and not driven by our thoughts. Just like we respond to our biological need to go to the bathroom or rest when we're tired, we can also respond without question or concern to our hunger needs. This means that we will feed ourselves and our family three solid meals a day with snacks as needed and know that eating every 3 to 4 hours is important to sustain energy levels throughout the day. Likewise, the typical 2,000 calorie-a-day diet promoted by the government is usually a vast underestimation of a female's body needs, especially those younger than 25. Researcher Gwyneth Olwyn recommends a minimum of 2,500 to 3500 calories per day based on age, height, and weight. This number may even be low if chronic restriction is the case and the body is coming back into balance.

* * *

MANTRA

- I will listen to my body and eat when I'm hungry.
- I don't need to ignore, trick, or negotiate with my body's hunger cues.
- I will feed myself and my family three solid meals a day at a minimum along with snacks. I will not go longer than 3 to 4 hours without eating food.

Challenge the Food Police

For the most part, we have very well-behaved kids, for all intents and purposes. Sure, they mess up in small ways, like yelling at me, squabbling with their siblings, forgetting their homework, and losing their patience, but we can usually count on them to listen, get their work done, and know right from wrong. Sometimes our kids get on each other's nerves and suddenly they're on high alert for any wrongdoing amongst them, ready to tell on one another at a moment's notice. My husband calls it the "looking to find blame" gene, which they may or may not have picked up from me! Sorry, kids, I'm just playing out my genetic lottery as the rule follower.

I, of course, appreciate the heads up when one of them tells me that our 2-year-old is lifting the dog by her hind legs to make her inadvertently do flips. However, my kids do not appreciate it when I get the heads up that they have a math test tomorrow and haven't studied. I'm sure you can relate. Maybe you have two kids who tag team with their mischievous plans or an only child who can happily play with their Magna-Tile tower with the assurance that an older or younger swiper won't smash it to smithereens. Many of us have one kid in the family that wears an imaginary police uniform and is constantly scanning their district for trouble. Who's not listening to Mom and Dad? Who's breaking the rules? Who's doing anything and everything wrong? Sound the sirens and release the dogs because these kids are on high alert so justice is served. They mean well; these cop kids feel it's their duty to help sustain family peace and ensure that their toys, projects, homework, and LEGO sets will be safe.

Kids aren't the only ones looking for trouble. Your brain is looking for safety, and that often comes in the form of a food cop patrolling your every move and morsel ingested. Do you ever feel like you have a silent (but very real and loud) food police officer running around your brain 24/7 questioning, commenting, admonishing or periodically high-fiving every morsel that does or doesn't go into your mouth?

"Why did you eat that?"

"What are you doing?"

"Who told you it was okay to eat that?"

"That's too much, illegal to touch, and, in general, bad for you."

"Just stop. You need to pull yourself together and be more disciplined."

"You need to get control. This is just food, and you're smarter than food."

"Good job skipping breakfast; you need to lose some fat on those thighs anyways."

Ouch. Who wants that constant feeling of dread with a running dialogue of beratement that triggers your shame and guilt? It's like having that pit in your stomach when you glance up in your rearview mirror, spot police squad lights spinning, and realize you're going 38 in a 25-mph zone. That feeling of terror mixed with fear is what the diet industry wants you to feel so that you'll keep buying their products and buying into their extraordinary scheme of lies.

How did this food police voice get so loud? How did you start

40

letting them constantly tell you what to do? Quite simply, the diet industry wants you to believe that you can't be trusted, you certainly can't be trusted around food, and you absolutely can't be trusted around making decisions when it comes to your body and food. The more you "learned" about diets, health, and nutrition, the louder this voice got.

Do you like the idea of someone constantly telling you what to do? Have your kid tell you what to do for 15 minutes today, and let me know how that feels. As a grown person, you probably don't like it when people tell you what to do. Well, as a professional dieter, you're doing just that. You are telling yourself exactly what, when, and how you should behave around food in order to reduce, maintain, or control your body size. Without knowing it, you've participated in your own oppression. You've taught yourself to distrust your own body. When you're constantly policing your kid around their choices with food, you're teaching them that they shouldn't be allowed to trust themselves either.

Diet culture tries appealing to your intellect by telling you that you're smarter than food! You can outwit your own body! You can find the "secret" to becoming thin forever! Guess what? The only thing you can outwit is the lies that you're being fed about diets, health, and food. Your body is so incredibly strong and smart, like a Google programmer times infinity smart, that no matter what you do or don't do, your body and food are going to be what they're going to be.

If you aren't listening to all the food rules and your inner cop, then what are you doing? Maybe it's time to participate in something else, like recognizing and dismantling the food rules you've created for yourself based on diet culture's lies fed to you by a system rooted in both patriarchy and racism. Start with breaking this basic rule that you can't eat what you want if you want to be healthy. You can, indeed, eat whatever you want. You aren't good or bad based on the number of calories or food you ate, and labeling your food as good or bad doesn't determine your level of worthiness. Eating certain foods may result in an unfavorable reaction that feels "bad" physically in your body, but food itself isn't bad.

Once you recognize your inner critic, pause and give them a name if that helps.

"Hey, it's you, Officer Cupcake. I know you're trying to protect me from getting out of control around food or eating something that will make my body change or my health worse."

You don't need to get rid of that voice because these voices are meant to help you in some way. This voice is loud because it's been fed misinformation over time. You can set it straight and challenge the voice so your intuitive voice can emerge more clearly.

"I hear what you're saying, but I don't need to believe what you're saying is true. I can listen to my intuition, which will naturally bring my body back into its own unique and intended balance; thank you very much."

When it comes to policing other people about their food, that's a hard NO. You can never know what's happening inside someone's body or be an accurate judge of what they should and shouldn't eat. We each have our own intricate wiring and genetics and history that leads us to need, want, and desire various foods and amounts of foods. Other people's food choices are not your business and not your "problem" to solve because food is never the problem in the first place. This is especially true for your kids. Once you offer the options at your dinner table, remember that any side commentary is off limits. (More about this later in the book.) You can remove your dinner cop uniform and actually enjoy conversation and connection at the table.

* * *

SUMMARY

On any given day, you have thousands of thoughts running through your head. You have hundreds of conversations with yourself, and some of them aren't true. Some of the voices you hear are parts of you that have been brainwashed by diet culture. Other voices think they're protecting you from weight gain by admonishing your every food move. Name these food police voices, acknowledge them, and move on. Listen instead to your intuitive voices around food and watch your food armor slowly slough off over time. Relaxing around food is possible when we stop believing that there's a right and wrong way to behave around food.

* * *

MANTRA

- I don't need to do what my inner critic is telling me to do.
- I can eat what I want when I want.
- Listening to my intuitive voice around food will bring me back to true freedom around food.

Are You Fatphobic?

An Uncomfortable Question

What happens when you field an uncomfortable question? What happens inside your body when you see a fat person? What runs through your mind?

Stay with me.

Be completely honest with yourself. Do you notice yourself thinking cruel, mean-spirited, judgmental, or even fearful thoughts about fat people?

Of course, you would never—EVER—say any of these thoughts aloud. Certainly not to their face. But privately, confidentially, deep inside… do nasty thoughts sometimes arise in your mind?

For instance, you see a larger-bodied person joining your Thursday night fitness class. Without knowing anything about them, you make a snap judgment. You think, "Oh great. Now the teacher is going to have to slow down the whole class and make things easier. We won't get a very good workout today."

You see a fat person ordering a cheeseburger, and internally you recoil, thinking, "Yikes. Seriously? That's your choice?" You take a smug forkful of your salad, feeling superior about your own body and food choices.

Your daughter comes home for a playdate with a new friend—who is significantly heavier than your kid. Again, while you would NEVER say anything aloud, there's a small part of you that's grateful your daughter is the slim one.

A larger-bodied person has a job interview at your workplace. Despite his numerous qualifications and great personality, a thought crosses your mind: "He's probably fat because he's lazy. He probably doesn't take good care of himself. He's probably in poor health—which will lead to lots of sick days. He's probably not the best candidate for the job. He probably has some deep-rooted trauma he hasn't dealt with that's led to his uncontrolled size."

Your partner has a new coworker and raves about how fantastic she is. You're pleased to discover that she's fat. "Good," you think to yourself. "She's not a threat to our marriage."

Do these kinds of thoughts ever cross your mind? Maybe quietly? Maybe loudly? Do you think these thoughts about yourself sometimes—directed toward your own body?

These are all examples of fatphobic thoughts.

These kinds of thoughts are destructive and harmful for everyone in our society—people of all sizes—and they're also unfair and untrue.

If you have fatphobic thoughts occasionally or even frequently, it doesn't mean you're a "bad" person. It just means that you—like virtually everyone else in our society—have been conditioned to believe that "thin is pure and good" and "fat is nasty and bad."

You've been fed the "fat is bad" message on a DAILY BASIS—practically since the day you were born—from movies, TV shows, magazines, and millions of commercials and marketing messages. You may have received fatphobic messages from the medical community (sadly, they're some of the worst culprits of body shaming and fatphobia), your parents, and other family members, too.

When you receive a specific message, millions upon millions of times, what happens? You get brainwashed. You become convinced. You believe that it's true, even if it's not.

It's time to replace the old fatphobic beliefs with new ones. This is a process of rewiring your mind. No, it's not easy, and yes, it takes awareness and commitment. But you can do it.

The very next time you notice a fatphobic thought crossing your mind, immediately INTERRUPT that thought, just like you would interrupt a bully who's harassing your son or daughter. *"Excuse me? Absolutely not. That kind of behavior is not welcome here."* Keep interrupting the fatphobic thoughts, over and over, whenever they arise. Remind yourself that the majority, if not all, of what you believe about people living in larger bodies isn't true. They aren't smelly and lazy. They are extremely intelligent, they actually don't eat more than thinner people and in many cases actually eat less food than thinner people, they do find loving and committed relationships, and they are valuable and important members of our society. Remind yourself that larger-bodied people have always existed over time and will continue to exist over time. Trying to eradicate a group of people by permanently altering their bodies would have been equivalent to telling a Bernese Mountain Dog to eat less food to take on more of a Poodle-like physique.

In this dog-eat-dog world of ours where we're willing to harm ourselves for supposed success, it's important to know that having fatphobic thoughts about other people almost always guarantees that you have fatphobic thoughts about yourself. Make sure you're interrupting fatphobic thoughts about yourself, too, and notice when your comments are hurtful and not helpful.

We can all build a better world—a world where NOBODY feels harassed, misunderstood, unfairly judged, ignored, overlooked, or bullied because of their size—and it starts on an individual level. It starts with me, with you, with our families, and what we teach our kids. Erasing fatphobia starts with the thoughts in our minds and educating ourselves that health happens across a spectrum and in bodies of all different shapes and sizes.

If you need some inspiration in seeing the beauty in and appreciating bodies of all sizes, I highly recommend the work of plus-size photographer and fat activist Lindley Ashline: www.bodylibera tionphotos.com.

* * *

SUMMARY

It's hard to admit when we've been unkind to ourselves or other people. It's even harder to admit that the reason we've been unkind is that we've been lied to about the truth and brainwashed into thinking certain stereotypes are true. People in larger bodies are very often pegged as being lazy, smelly, dirty, unmotivated, unlovable, irresponsible, riddled with some deep, dark trauma, or gluttonous pigs. Nothing could be further from the truth. People with bodies of all sizes run the gamut of intelligence, motivation, the amount of food they eat, how much they move their bodies, how sanitary they are, and whether they're in a committed relationship. I encourage you to look closely at some tightly held beliefs that simply aren't true. I invite you to look at all bodies neutrally and without judgment and see how changing your view of others can help you find more peace within your own body.

* * *

- I will not unfairly judge people in larger bodies.
- I will not continue to believe thoughts that aren't based on the truth.
- I will look to find the beauty in all bodies.

Listen to Your Cravings

What foods does your body crave the most? Can you think back to certain times in your life when your cravings were clear and persistent?

My pregnancies have been a treasure trove of learning around cravings. One of the most distinct cravings I remember having was root beer floats. My mouth practically salivated for that frothy, bubbly, creamy goodness. For some pregnancies, I wanted saltier foods; others, I wanted sweeter foods; and for all of them, I just wanted to stop feeling so nauseous from 12 p.m. to 12 a.m.! Getting anything down during those early days was the goal.

Because food aversions were so strong during pregnancy, it was a great time to really identify what I liked and what worked for me on any given day, at any given time of day. I didn't have the luxury of finding alternatives because what I wanted was usually very specific, with no substitutions allowed. Ramen noodles and Ritz crackers or bust!

I used to feel like my goal was to constantly find substitutions or a "healthier" alternative to the food I really wanted. Think rice cakes instead of potato chips or a frozen banana instead of ice cream. I didn't think "allowing" myself to have what I really wanted was the worthy, wise, or weight-gain-prevention strategy I needed, so I'd force myself to choose the more virtuous item.

But do you know what happens when you don't listen to your needs? You find yourself elbow-deep in a bag of chocolate chips at 11 o'clock at night because you'd been craving chocolate all day but kept telling yourself that the carob chips or that some vegan, protein, chocolate powder mixed into some warm milk would do the trick. It just doesn't work.

Your body is an incredibly smart instrument, constantly giving you cues and clues for what it needs most. Think of it like your persistent toddler who knows that they just HAVE to wear those pink pants or that truck shirt or that sequin flip shirt to school or they'll refuse to get in the car or on the bus. As parents, we know better than to argue; we usually say, okay, go for it! This is the same attitude that we want to adopt with our food. So you want noodles and ketchup? Go for it! Sounds like a great combination.

What if you wake up one day and crave a croissant from your local bakery? Why not allow yourself to go get it! Wanting that fresh mixed salad for lunch? Time to whip it up. Already tasting some perfectly grilled steak tips and potatoes for dinner? Fabulous. Wanting a quick trip to the drive-through for your favorite drink/burger/ice cream/chicken fingers/fries? Guess what? It's okay to say yes to your body because your cravings are like your own personal map leading you in the direction of satiety both physically (my tummy is full) and emotionally (my brain is telling me I'm all set here). Enjoy food when you want and with a sense of sheer joy and zero guilt.

Maybe you're reading this thinking you don't have any cravings or desires around food. If you've been disconnected from your body for any period of time, this isn't a surprise. It might take you some time to rediscover what you crave once you give yourself the proverbial green light to enjoy anything your heart desires. Practice seeing all food as neutral (because it is), and invite yourself to relax instead of tense up around food. Eventually your food choices and your body will start to communicate with you. Eating three meals a day plus desired snacks will help open those doors of communication as well.

What if you're wondering about your kid who has the same cravings or desires around food every day, like buttered noodles at every meal? Maybe they've gone through a period of only eating food that's one color. It's actually fine to offer one or two "safe" foods at every meal so there's always something available for your kid to eat. Keep offering a variety of items and know that taste buds and desired foods do change. Kids get the nutrients they need over a period of time and not at any one particular meal.

Avoid any pressure techniques, no matter how subversive you think they might be… "Don't these carrots look delicious?" "Doesn't that broccoli look yummy?" Or: "I worked so hard to make you dinner. Can't you just have a no-thank-you bite?" All of these tactics will actually backfire in the long run, so fasten your seat belt and have faith that your child's food palette will expand over time. I think about how I used to think avocados were gross (slimy texture!) and now I love them. Talk to your child about how your tastes have changed, and remember that you likely started with a narrower palate, too. Remember that kids are very smart, and they know what foods will give them the energy they need.

If you're truly concerned about your kid's intake being limited or suspect they struggle with ARFID (Avoidant Restrictive Food Intake Disorder), seek out a HAES-friendly dietitian who can help you create a specific plan for your needs. Showing your kid how to honor their desires around food can help them well beyond the dinner table. Maybe someday they'll have a desire to travel to Spain, so you decide to help them follow that desire by researching and figuring out a way to make that possible. It's our unique desires that create our unique path in life. Denying desires both around food and elsewhere in our lives can lead to decreased joy, confidence, and satisfaction.

* * *

SUMMARY

Recognizing your needs and desires around food and honoring those needs can feel a little scary at times, especially if you have a history of dieting. Showing your kid that you feel safe and comfortable honoring these desires is a really important lesson for both you and your kid to experience. Your kid can be a great teacher around desires. Thankfully, they've lived in a diet culture for a shorter time and hopefully don't have as many deeply rooted fears around allowance with food as you do. Enjoy this proverbial green light you've been granted around all foods and see where your desires take you!

* * *

MANTRA

- I will allow myself to enjoy the foods I desire.
- Honoring my desires is vital to my well-being.
- I choose to listen and respond to my body's requests. It is my birthright to enjoy the foods I desire.

Section 2

Proactive Parenting in the Face of Diet Culture

The Importance of Meals and Snacks

I'm amazed at the amount of energy our kids have. The pink Energizer Bunny running in circles beating on a drum comes to mind as a match for their output. They can run from one activity to the next and put everything they've got into a playdate, soccer game, trampoline jump session, and more. We're often reminding them that they need to rest before they run off to their second sporting event of the day.

I'm guessing your kids, like ours, can run (literally) from activity to activity without skipping a beat and are still jumping on the bed and throwing pillows with the strength of a superhero at 8:10 p.m. While we're ready to say lights out before our kids, their little bodies are still on the move. It's no wonder that kids are often, or even constantly, eating!

The rate of exponential growth for kids coupled with their energy expenditure means they need to be fed consistently and enough throughout the day. A piece of fruit or some graham crackers as a quick meal just isn't going to cut it for you or your kids. Meals should have all the major food groups: carbohydrates, protein, fat, and bonus points for fiber. I always think in simple terms of a grain, a protein/meat, and a veggie. I like to reflect back to the family dinners my grandmother would have cooked for our entire family. Full, hearty meals are the goal, but we all also know that cereal for dinner happens sometimes too. And that's a-okay. Please remember that something is always better than nothing.

Kids really do need three meals a day. Breakfast, lunch, and dinner provide the backbone of our daily routine, and we pepper in a morning and afternoon snack, too. Your job isn't to control your child's weight or control their intake so that it looks "perfect." Your job is simply to provide food (even for teens) in a safe and nurturing environment. Banning words like guilt-free or cheat day around family eating is so important to maintaining a safe environment so kids experience every day as a day to eat until satisfaction. If you've ever had a toddler melting down at 11:10 a.m., think back to whether you offered a snack that morning. Food helps little ones (and adults) sustain both their physical and mental energy and forgetting food can very often lead to a dysregulated child.

Even though you might be tempted to skip breakfast (or grab a bite of something here or there) because you're too busy or because you're not hungry, you and your kids shouldn't skip meals for any reason. Feeding yourself regularly assures you and your body that you have plenty of food and energy to meet your daily needs. Without regular meals and enough energy/intake, your kid's body will move into starvation mode, which means their energy levels, mood, and growth can be negatively affected. Over prolonged periods of food restriction, critical systems shut down. The reproductive system, digestion, and metabolism slow down; hair and nails become brittle and weak; temperature regulation slows (meaning the body gets cold and stays cold easily); mood worsens, and energy levels decrease. Even skipping a snack or not having food for several hours in a single day can send your kid into massive meltdown mode.

A growing kid who's trying to concentrate at school must have three regular meals at a minimum. Providing two to three additional snacks is optional but also recommended. Kids have smaller stomachs than adults and often need food every 3 to 4 hours. I don't recommend going beyond the 4-hour mark between meals or snacks for adults or kids. Providing regular food throughout the day is crucial for optimal health and growth, and sitting with your child at as many of these meals, especially dinner, as possible can have health effects far beyond a safe and nurturing relationship with food.

A stack of studies have shown that family dinners resulted in improved academic performance at school and a reduction of high-risk teen behaviors like drinking, smoking, marijuana use, violence, school problems, and disordered eating. Mealtime should be away from electronic devices (yes, you, too, need to put your phone down) and be free from tense or stressful interactions. Doing this will provide a time for meaningful connection, important bonding within families, and positive experiences that will last beyond the table. Roast chicken, rice, and vegetables are great, but so is macaroni and cheese with frozen peas and a piece of fruit. As long as there's enough food from a variety of food groups, the content is less important. A home-cooked meal or a drive-through dinner both get the job done.

* * *

SUMMARY

One of the best things you can do for your child is provide them with three full meals a day and snacks as needed. Meals don't need to be grand or take a lot of time to prepare, they just need to be available! Yes, it does take time to think about the million-dollar question of what's for dinner, but it's worth putting some time into this part of parenting. A combination of carbohydrates, protein, and fat (bonus for fiber) is best. Don't skip meals or let you or your child go more than 4 hours without food. Once you've served your meal and are letting your child decide how much and what they want, pull up a seat. Sitting with your child to enjoy meals has been shown to have a slew of positive effects, most notably a reduction in high-risk teen behaviors.

* * *

MANTRA

- Having three full meals a day is important for me and my family.
- Making snacks available between meals is important.
- I will make sure I and my family get enough to eat throughout the day.

Digital Detox

I sat in the backseat with my cantankerous toddler, trying to settle him (and me) down for the rest of the already too-long car ride. After going through my basket of toys in a matter of minutes, I asked my husband in an exasperated voice to put the Peppa Pig (a British-based cartoon starring various pig characters) DVD in…NOW. My son was immediately at ease and got that unmistakable technology trance, staring wide-eyed with his mouth slightly open. I breathed a sigh of relief, said a silent thank you to technology in my mind, and started watching with my son.

Within minutes, though, my relief turned to frustration as I watched one of the main characters of this cartoon—Daddy Pig—being fat-shamed by his family. Everyone was having a good laugh at Daddy Pig's expense, saying he sits on the couch too much, has too big a belly (we're talking about pigs here, after all), and doesn't eat enough vegetables. The unfortunate truth is that fatphobia (irrational fear of, aversion to, or discrimination against larger-bodied people) messages run deep, are literally everywhere, and have no age limits.

And unfortunately, fatphobic content isn't the only problematic messaging in the media our kids consume.

Have you ever taken a critical look at the media in your home that you and your kids watch/read/hear? Magazines with airbrushed cover models, books with stereotypical character portrayal of the thin pretty girl getting the cute date or the larger character who got that way by eating too much food, TV shows with cheap jokes about larger-bodied people. The struggle is real to keep this toxic and misleading media information from filtering through your home. Click on any website, scroll through any social media tab, and within seconds, you're staring at a commercial or ad for some weight loss product, plan, or promotion.

While it's nearly impossible to get rid of all media messaging, it's worth the effort to regularly and systematically take a critical eye to what you and your family do consume. Evaluate your magazine subscriptions, for instance, and ask yourself if the images are telling a story you want your child unconsciously believing. You could even take a more proactive approach and look at the photos with your child and explain that virtually NONE of them are real. Everyone has been airbrushed, touched up, enhanced, faded, or smoothed to get that "perfect" look. I'll even go so far as to point out to our kids people in real life who have been enhanced in some way. There's no shame in having plastic surgery; you do you. The problem is there's shame in feeling like you'll never measure up to other bodies that appear to have all the stereotypical curves, yet the irony is many of these bodies have been surgically altered in the first place. I also encourage you to actively watch shows with your kids so you can point out fatphobic messaging and teach kids that commercials are largely in place to get the viewer to buy certain products and to think critically about those messages, too.

Since we can't truly escape the reaches of diet culture, we can at least educate ourselves and our kids. Ask yourself what's real. Ask your kids what they think about pictures, shows, and billboards. Ask your kid what their definition of beauty is. Have your kid start recognizing the truth about messaging around food and body. The good news is that you'll have multiple opportunities throughout the day, trust me. The even better news is that you can break the generations-long dieting tradition that may have existed in your family until right now. You can be a cycle breaker by not buying into what you see in the media, hear on the television, or read in a book. Let's turn our exasperation into some action that will someday leave the diet industry gaping with eyes wide and mouths slightly open at the number of anti-dieters who simply won't believe their lies anymore and demand a more socially just and inclusive conversation around body size, health and equality for all.

* * *

SUMMARY

It's hard to go a day without being completely bombarded by fatphobic messages on the television, on the radio, in magazines, online, and in literature for all ages. While it's nearly impossible to stop this messaging, it's important to think critically about what you see, hear, and believe. Eliminating outright fatphobic messaging that comes to your home on a regular basis can be a great start. With diet culture infiltrating every corner of our lives, like germs from the flu, I encourage you to actively watch, read, and listen with your kids to help them sort fact from fiction. Knowing what's real, what's fake, and what messaging is simply meant to ignite your shame and fear like a match to gasoline so you buy their product, you can make a difference for yourself and your kid.

* * *

MANTRA

- It's up to me to allow the best possible information into my home.
- I don't need to believe everything (or anything) that's being sold by diet culture.
- I will have honest conversations in my home about fatphobia in our culture.

Diversify Your Social Media Feed

Have you ever stopped to wonder how you feel after minutes or hours of scrolling through your social media feeds? When you look up at the clock or glance at your watch in surprise at how much time slips by so easily once you turn your attention to these sites, it can feel a little unsettling. Who hasn't fallen prey to the slick slip-n-slide of easy entertainment to dull the edges of daily boredom with an easy hit of dopamine? Do you walk away from these sessions feeling energized and inspired? Or does some part of you feel a little uneasy?

Screen time, social media usage, and technology allowances are all personal choices, and regardless of your stance, awareness is key. I recently decided that social media isn't where I want to spend my time. With six kids, every minute is precious, and I noticed that I wasn't walking away from time spent on social media feeling good or filled up. Leaving has been a welcome change for me.

Assuming you're 40 years old, if you spend just 20 minutes a day on social media and live until you're 80 years old, you'll spend close to a year scrolling on your phone. A YEAR! What would you do if someone told you that you could get an extra year in your life? How would you spend that time? That said, I still have accounts on two social media sites for the sole purpose of looking things up when I want to and selling items on Facebook Marketplace. But I do so with intention, and I know that, just like my food, things in life don't have to be black and white.

If you've decided that social media is going to be a part of your life, I encourage you to do a quick wash and rinse of your account, a little shampoo to the system. Notice who you follow. Notice which accounts leave you feeling less than for any reason and which accounts leave you feeling supported just the way you are. When you constantly look at one particular body size, you literally train your brain to see that as the only size that is acceptable, worthy, beautiful, and valuable.

Diversifying your feed can be a really important way to re-educate your brain. When you look at images of people that are your size or larger, you redefine "normal." Finding ways to see beauty in all body types can be a really great way to expand your definition of beauty. Your account can include all sizes, ages, abilities, ethnicities, gender identities, and BIPOC individuals. Take a solid look at fitspo (fitness/sports) influencers in your feed, as they're notorious for being a source of unrealistic reminders of body size and food perfection. Not only is the "perfect" body subjective, viewing these images repetitively over time can negatively influence your self-image and self-worth.

Helping your child diversify their feed can be a helpful exercise, too. The Facebook whistleblower, Frances Haugen, was quoted in a U.S. News & World Report article as saying, "Facebook knows that vulnerable people are harmed by its systems, like kids who are susceptible to feel bad about their bodies because of Instagram." Knowing our children are being targeted makes it even more important for us to sit with and talk to our kids, especially teenage girls, about the potential harms of spending time on these sites. Talking with kids about the unrealistic images portrayed and how marketers make it their job to prey on their fears and inadequacies so that they profit off of their insecurities is so important.

At the back of this book, you'll find a link to a list of body positive accounts that can help you diversify and detoxify your feed.

* * *

SUMMARY

Taking a good look at your social media habits can profoundly affect the way you feel about yourself and how you view others. If social media is important to you, I encourage you to detox your digital feed and only follow influencers, businesses, or individuals that promote body and self-acceptance. Seeing people of your size or larger is an important step in really seeing yourself as worthy and valuable. Sit with your kid and review their social media accounts, and talk to them about diet culture's unrealistic standards. Encourage your kids to edit who and what they follow in the digital world.

* * *

MANTRA

- My body is never the problem; diet culture is the problem.
- I can find beauty in many bodies.
- All bodies are good bodies.

When Your Kid is
Sneaking/Hiding Food

Tidying up around the house before friends arrived, I ran frantically from room to room to do the one-arm sweep of kids' toys and gadgets into drawers. I opened my then 8-year-old daughter's nightstand to shove in some random papers and stopped dead in my tracks. The drawer was littered with a bunch of empty candy wrappers.

With an older kid, I wouldn't have cared that much. Older kids start treating their room like their own apartment and periodically take their food into their safe space just to chill or do homework. At this young age, though, I knew this was about her not feeling like she could eat candy in front of her parents without feeling embarrassed or getting reprimanded. It felt like a massive mom-fail moment for me, and I had to be tender with myself as I problem-solved how to make positive change. The last thing I wanted was for my kids to feel like they had to sneak their food like a mouse scampering into a dark corner because they felt any sort of shame or embarrassment around food or were being deprived of certain foods.

As soon as I found these wrappers, I called a family meeting. Imagine a queen at her throne addressing her royal subjects by announcing (with a British accent, of course) that from this day forth, these children shall be allowed to eat dessert every night. The crowd inevitably erupted with whoops and hollers of delight.

"Really?! Are you serious, Mom? Yesssss!"

At the time of my wrapper discovery, we had a "dessert only on weekends" rule at our house that had been born from a late-afternoon grocery store trip with my very hungry kids. They had been peppering me nonstop with requests for every sweet and processed food they could get their hands on. I was still in my "lifestyle" eating days and trying to make all the "good" and "healthy" choices for our family, desperate to keep "junk" foods out of the house. As I was dragging the kids down the final aisle, I heard a fellow mom say to her kid, "Nope, you can't have that now, but I can save it for dessert night this weekend." I ran with the idea and implemented it immediately. Anything to stop the constant whining, begging, and nagging was a win in my book.

Except it wasn't a win at all. The promise of weekend desserts may have quieted our kids down in the grocery store that evening, but it quieted something even more fundamental—their joy, desire, and pleasure when it comes to food. It signaled to them that certain foods were special and had to be "earned" in some way.

Transitioning back to "yes" from that season of "no" felt like a much-needed exhale. I've noticed how much the kids who experienced that restriction have relaxed around food. We do enjoy sweet food most nights at our house and have since that day. Our kids haven't necessarily changed body size, haven't had their sleep affected, and their behavior hasn't gone bananas because of what they eat. Some mornings, one of our kids will wake up and say, "Oh no, I forgot to eat dessert last night!" because they aren't constantly focused on something that's readily available to them throughout the week.

When you give full allowance, food really does lose its siren song calling you at all hours of the day, especially at night. I simply decided that arguments over food aren't where I want to devote my energy and precious interactions with our kids. I didn't want my kids to have memories of feeling shame or embarrassment around eating any type or amount of food. I didn't want them to feel like they had to go to friends' houses to get the food they wanted, and I didn't want them to feel out of control or afraid outside of our home around foods that had been restricted from them—even if I thought it was for a good reason.

A note about teenage kids and food. It's totally normal for them to want to stop at a store like CVS, Starbucks, or a gas station to get some food with their friends. The options for kids to practice independence within walking distance from your home or school can be limited depending on your location. It's a good experience for your teen to have to manage some money, interact with an adult to order, or pay for food and experiment with what foods they enjoy or want to eat. There could be much worse things that your kids are getting into, so if Dunkin' is a daily stop, it's really not the end of the world!

* * *

SUMMARY

When kids hide their food, it can be a sign they feel embarrassed or ashamed to eat certain foods in front of others because they've been shamed about those foods or had their food restricted. This might be from rules and regulations you've placed around food and very likely has something to do with deprivation. Food scarcity can also be at play for kids who aren't secure in the amount of food they'll receive on any given day. To avoid this behavior, I encourage you to give full allowance around food in your home. Instead of making foods out to have moral values like good and bad, treat all foods as equal. There aren't foods that are better than others, and trust that your kid will make choices that reflect their tastes and deep biological needs around food. Know that your kids will find the foods that feel good and give them the energy they need.

* * *

MANTRA

- I will give my child full allowance when it comes to food.
- I will not make my child feel embarrassed or ashamed about any food they eat.
- I will promote joy and pleasure around food and treat foods neutrally.

What Your Kids See You Eat Matters

One of my kids and I have this almost psychic connection. I have an injury on my foot, and she has the same injury a couple of days later. She comes to me complaining of a sore muscle, and lo and behold, that very same muscle is sore on me, too. It's a little bit spooky, like our umbilical cord connection is still exchanging information. But I've also noticed how much my food choices influence her.

When I was breastfeeding, my doctor suggested I cut dairy to help with the colic my baby was experiencing. While I don't personally have a dairy allergy, I was happy to make the accommodation to seek some relief for my incredibly fussy baby (think vacuum cleaners at 2 a.m. to soothe the screaming baby strapped to my chest). It eventually became a habit for me, which meant that even though I wasn't breastfeeding, I was still avoiding dairy years later. One day I noticed that my daughter was starting to avoid dairy, too. I was used to her and I having a connection, but this felt like a new level of mimicry. Not wanting her to avoid foods because of my example, I started adding dairy back into my meals, and I encouraged her to do the same.

Maybe you've noticed this in your own home if you've ever

announced a new eating plan or vowed to avoid eating a certain food type for whatever reason. Even if it doesn't seem like it, our kids are constantly looking to us for guidance around food. They pretend they don't want or need our guidance, but in reality they need us and the good example we can set by feeling relaxed and joyful around food. With this in mind, I invite you to think about these questions.

Do you eat the same thing every day? Do you only eat salads and grilled chicken and drink coffee with MCT oil or beverages spiked with collagen powder? Have you cut out entire food groups without having a medically diagnosed food allergy? Are you restricting your intake (no matter how small you think your restriction is)? Do you shun dessert or sugar of any kind?

Having tense or nervous energy around food can be felt and cause a growing kid who is in their critical stages of development to be concerned or frightful about their food choices. When preparing foods, make sure you have a variety of grains, fruits, vegetables, beans, seeds, fats, and sweets. Don't be afraid to enjoy freshly baked cookies or brownies or delight in ice cream on a hot summer day and a steaming cup of hot chocolate during the winter. Better yet, take some time to sit with your kid during meals or snacks as a way to show them that food is meant to be enjoyed and can be a powerful connection tool. Doing this will help your kid feel safe and relaxed around food. They will sense that food isn't something to be feared, isn't a measure of your (or their) worth or value, and isn't something that can kill or cure us.

Summary

To put it bluntly, you're being watched all the time. Your kids are looking to you for guidance on how to do this thing called life, and food is no different. What a gift for your kid to see that you are relaxed around food and are comfortable eating a variety of foods. Eating with your kid is another way to show them that food is meant to be enjoyed with others, and there's never anything to hide or be embarrassed about when it comes to how much you eat or your food choices.

Mantra

- I can enjoy a variety of foods without guilt.
- I am free to pick any foods that I want and not have to hide my choices.
- I will enjoy food with my child as one of the many ways we can connect.

Find Joy and Pleasure in Food

My daughter, mom, and I were covered in flour as we happily mixed, rolled, shaped, and cut out our traditional Italian Easter cookies. My daughter delighted in pouring cups of what, to her, must have seemed like magic dust into the bowls. She giggled as she watched the mixer crank the batter into Play-Doh-like cookie dough and was thrilled to have her kid's knife to help shape our bunnies, baskets, and baby chicks. Three generations together learning, laughing, and loving. Sampling our freshly baked sugar cookies left us all with that warm feeling of joy only a hot-from-the-oven cookie can provide. I thought to myself, "It doesn't get much better than this."

I delight in watching our kids get excited about all different kinds of foods they want to enjoy, whether it's hot cinnamon rolls fresh out of the oven, freshly baked chocolate chip cookies, my mom's famous baked pasta, or a new ice cream creation with rainbow sprinkles and cocoa powder. I'm constantly reminded that food really is fun and joyful and provides pleasure. Remember, a big part of our innate biology is meant to enjoy food so we're incentivized to eat it for survival.

Thinking back to school, it never seemed like the message around food was fun. It was simply, here's the giant poster with the food pyramid and here's how things are categorized. You should eat based on selecting the right type and amount of food from these categories, and don't eat anymore. The end.

No wonder, as adults, we approach food in such a pragmatic and joyless manner. Food isn't viewed as the life-giving force it is. It's viewed as a means to an end or a means to get to a more preferred (albeit nearly impossible) end. I'm so grateful that my big Italian family showed me the opposite. They centered celebrations around food, which was a form of connection, pride, love, and even a career, as my grandparents owned and operated a food catering business. The sound of laughter and feelings of belonging with my cousins, aunts, and uncles from our weekly Sunday night dinners remains one of my best childhood memories.

Somewhere along our life path, we've internalized the idea that food is "bad" in some way because it contributes to our body size, which we've been programmed to believe determines our worth, value, happiness, and health. While our size doesn't actually determine any piece of our character, there are real barriers that people living in larger bodies experience, including finding general comfort inside and outside of the home, dealing with difficult travel accommodations, facing fatphobic doctors and nurses in healthcare, finding clothing, having equal employment opportunities, receiving fair and appropriate insurance, and receiving different salaries because of size discrimination. It's no wonder food has been demonized instead of celebrated or even revered for its life-giving properties.

Food is meant to be enjoyed and celebrated together in the company of friends and family. It's normal and natural to find pleasure in many foods. If you feel like food is lacking in joy or pleasure in your life, I invite you to think back to your childhood. Is there a food that brings all the good memories flooding back to you? For me, it's peanut butter and jelly sandwiches, my nana's pasta, Christmas cookies, and late-night bowls of graham crackers, ice cream, and milk with my dad.

I encourage you to see food through the eyes of a young child. See their sheer joy, hear their squeals of excitement, and feel their good vibes as they unwrap a lollipop, take their first sip of hot chocolate, or pop some freshly popped popcorn into their mouth. Sometimes I'll find my kids running laps around our kitchen island in anticipation of something delicious coming their way. Have you ever been to an ice cream store and watched waiting kids literally doing a dance of joy as they wait for their creamy, flavor-packed, cold ice cream? Have you ever planted something and waited in joyful anticipation of enjoying a fresh, delicious garden-grown delight? It's my hope that you can find some of that same joy and excitement around your food again and teach your children to find the same.

While eating certain foods does release chemicals in the brain that affect our emotions, these are the same chemicals released when we listen to music or give/receive hugs or snuggle a puppy or newborn baby. There's no such thing as food addiction (more on that soon), so eat with gusto! Eating foods that don't give you any sense of pleasure is a form of restriction, and restriction on any level will lead you to binge eating at some point down the road.

Even though it might be scary, have fun reconnecting with some of your favorite foods that you may have labeled forbidden or deemed inferior during your diet-culture filled years. Dieters often feel a sense of pride or superiority because of their ability to restrict, forbid, and avoid various foods and have to process feelings of inferiority when going back to some food favorites. You'll not be more virtuous because you're able to avoid certain foods; you'll just be more miserable in the long run. There's value in eating foods that feel good in your body and taste delicious. I encourage you to think of finding joy and pleasure in food as an essential act of self-care.

* * *

SUMMARY

For hundreds and thousands of years, food has been a source of joy and pleasure that helps bring people together to share in community and togetherness. If you've dieted for any period of time, there's a good chance that food has lost a little (or a lot) of pleasure as you likely treated food as a transaction or negotiation and not something to delight in. I encourage you to reconnect with your inner child to find what foods bring you joy and pleasure and create a whole new relationship with food that feels less transactional and more blissful. Keep shedding away old diet rules and regulations and keep allowing for more relaxation and glee around food, and maybe, just maybe, the joy and pleasure you experience in your life will increase more than you imagined.

* * *

MANTRA

- Food is meant to provide joy and pleasure.
- I can enjoy any foods I want with a sense of gusto.
- I can let go of rules around food and allow myself to relax around food.

Give Yourself Permission to Be Imperfect

My son was bubbling with excitement to make a card for his classmate's birthday party. His present was tucked in a sky blue gift bag, and the final touch was to write his friend's name on the card. With #2 pencil in hand, he happily worked away as I spelled out the birthday boy's name.

Suddenly he hollered out in agony, and the #2 pencil took flight.

"Okay, buddy, what's going on?" I asked, already knowing the answer.

"I messed up my letter!" he shouted in disgust.

After acknowledging that he felt sad about that, I offered to have him play the gooble or no gooble game with me. At school, he learned this game as a fun way to see if the teacher was writing a letter correctly or incorrectly. I said we were going to do a big gooble, and he could write his friend's name, but only ONE letter could be correct, and I had to find it amidst the goobled letters.

"Did you know that you learn more from making mistakes than not making mistakes?" I said, although I don't even think he heard or cared because he was too busy goobling letters.

He came to me a couple of minutes later with a huge grin and said, "I bet you can't find it, Mommy!"

He then went back to the card and wrote happily on his own. He showed me the final product with a crooked "S," and we both agreed it looked just right.

I, too, used to get frustrated when things weren't right or absolutely perfect. I think we all struggle with perfectionistic tendencies, some more than others, and for many, this is just hardwired into our DNA (*raises hand*). Having perfectionist tendencies around food can be really tricky because there are so many opportunities to not get things "right," even though there's no right or wrong way to perform when it comes to food.

Instead of trying to eliminate our perfectionistic tendencies, we can simply NOTICE them and name them. *"Oh, hey, you, perfect Patty (or whatever name you want to give your inner critic voice). I see you. I hear you. I'm going to just do my best here, which means listening to and respecting my body's needs. Nothing, especially my food, needs to be perfect."*

When you hear the critical voice, author Ethan Kross recommends taking a bird's eye view of the situation. What advice would you give a friend standing in your shoes? What do you see happening from a fly on the wall perspective that can give you some clarity and alleviate some of your self-imposed pressures?

I get that it can be a hard switch to make. From the minute our babies are born, there's pressure to do it all perfectly. Get the perfect crib, the best swaddle, the best bottle, the best pacifier, the best toys, the best of it all. This perfectionistic pressure oozes right into how we should be feeding our babies and kids—all organic foods, homemade purées, not too many carbs, only grass-fed, free-range meats, if any meat at all, and no sugar. We often feel that we're falling short as a parent if we do anything less, like bringing home a bag of Dunkin' for breakfast or hitting the drive-through on the way home. It's literally impossible to keep up with a perfectionistic performance attitude around food.

Instead of trying to keep up with the Joneses or diet culture's fantasy way of eating, stop and think about what your values are as an individual and as a family. Ask yourself: *Where did I get these messages about the pressure I'm placing on food? What happens if I can trust myself and eliminate the constant noise from so-called experts?*

When you catch yourself trying to act perfectly around food, pause and go within, and ask yourself what you need and what's possible in this moment. You might not have time to cook a meal, and fast food would do the job. You don't need external approval for eating anything at any time.

Rest assured, there isn't any one food or meal that can permanently harm you. You know what tastes and feels good for your body, and if you feel like you've lost touch with your true wants, have some fun playing around with old and new foods. Just like I shared with my son during his letter-writing snafu, we all learn more from our "failures" (you really can't fail around food, EVER) than we do our "perfect" days of eating. A simple "oops, that didn't work for my body" is all you need to register what didn't go well and that you might want to change course in the future. Maybe that amount of food wasn't so great right before bed, or maybe that sugar crash in the afternoon could be avoided by adding in more protein next time you eat a chocolate bar at 3 p.m. Food goobles are not a big deal and are a way for you to get to know yourself and understand your body on a deeper level.

When you give yourself permission to be imperfect, you're much more willing to experiment with foods, explore what works best for you, and cut yourself some slack when you don't or can't get a home-cooked meal on the table. Some parents work multiple jobs to support their families, and the best they can do with their time and financial resources is a box of macaroni, canned beans or soup, a frozen entree, or a trip to the drive-through, and that's perfectly okay. That doesn't make them less than or bad in any way.

Go ahead, take your #2 pencil, and write out a new way of eating for yourself and your family. Make some mistakes while you're at it, too. Food rules are arbitrary and meant to be broken.

* * *

SUMMARY

Diet culture wants us to believe that there's a certain way to act or perform around food. This mythical performative standard disconnects us from our bodies. You know what's best for your body, and you can enjoy a variety of foods without causing any physical harm. What's harmful is when your mental health is adversely affected by your perfectionistic tendencies. Give yourself permission to relax and connect with your body. Trust yourself and your kid to make the right choices when it comes to food, and rest assured that your body is incredibly smart and able to adapt hunger levels to match your body's needs.

* * *

MANTRA

- I don't have to be perfect around food.
- There's no such thing as failure when it comes to food.
- There's no right or wrong way to do food. I trust myself to know what's best for me and my body.

Section 3

Talking to Your Kid About Their Body

Never Shame Your Kid's Body Size

My daughter peered into my eyes and asked me what color they were.

"I have brown eyes," I said matter-of-factly.

"I have blue eyes!" she cheered.

"Yes, you and Daddy and your brother have blue eyes, and everyone else has brown or hazel eyes."

She looked at me very concerned and said, "Change it now!"

"I wish I could, but I can't change my eye color. All eyes are pretty and different, and that's okay with Mommy if we don't have the same eye color. Is that okay with you?"

"Yes, it's good. I like those, too, Mommy."

Sure, I'd love to have piercing blue eyes, but it's just not what the genetic lottery gave me. So I've got Van Morrison's song to dance to at weddings and a long line of relatives with the same eye color as me. It is what it is. But why don't we view body size like our other physical characteristics?

Diet culture has made larger bodies "bad" and encourages everyone to change their size despite no research supporting permanent body change as a viable possibility. There's no crusade against hair color, height, shoe size, and eye color. These are simply characteristics that we can't change (save for color contacts or hair dye). Yet diet culture wants us to believe that with a little grit and determination we can change our body size now, despite there being no evidence that sustained weight loss works.

One of the things you can work on is being committed to keeping weight out of your conversations at home, especially with your kids. This is even more important if one or more of your kids falls outside of society's arbitrary "normal" for body size. One of our kids has a solid frame. He's strong and a great athlete. Sometimes relatives or friends go out of their way to say that he's a BIG kid. Instead of trying to contradict their statement, I remind them and my son that he's strong and his body can do a lot of amazing things and that there's nothing wrong with his size. I also like to remind him about his character—how he's a kind friend who gives the best hugs and how he makes me laugh. I don't want him to think that big is bad, so I purposely don't say, "Oh no, you're not big!" It's when we give kids the message that big is bad that it becomes a problem. If I argued against those comments and said, "Don't worry, you're not big," my son would start to think that being bigger was in some way wrong or bad. No kid asked for their body size and no kid should be made to feel less than no matter where they fall on the size charts. Thanks to genetics, all bodies will be what they're going to be, and it's our job as parents to support and love our kids regardless of their shape.

Even comments like, "Oh, she's so little!" can be hard for a kid to hear. Someday they might not be little, and they might tie positive attention they received to having a small size and feel badly about their new, bigger size. It can be innocent comments like these that sting and stick the most.

A great kid's book on this topic is called *Shapesville*. The gist of the story is that squares, triangles, circles, and rectangles are all welcome, and there's no need to force a square peg into a round hole!

It's like the shape-sorting toy from your toddler days. Just like the toy pieces, everybody should have a place where they feel they belong.

My other favorite is *Bodies Are Cool* by Tyler Feder, which shows a diverse range of sizes, abilities, genders, and colors to help normalize what most bodies in America look like. Hello, chin hairs! You might be surprised to learn that 60% of the population has a larger body. You might think that everyone looks like a waif model based on what you're bombarded with on the news, on television, in magazines, and on social media, but it's simply not true. A size 4 isn't a medium. A size 16/18 should actually be considered a true medium based on our population's actual sizes.

In addition to keeping weight or body size out of the conversation with your kids, it's important to avoid commenting on your child's weight gain or weight loss. Implying that they look good or better with weight loss or suddenly limiting/monitoring their food with weight gain are both the wrong messages. If you do notice a large amount of weight loss or gain in a short period of time and have some concerns, talking with your child's doctor in private before bringing them in for a checkup is recommended. This can be a delicate subject, especially if your child is feeling self-conscious about weight changes, which is why I encourage conversations about weight to happen out of the kid's earshot.

It's also important to engage your child by asking general questions outside of weight, like how are you feeling? How do you feel like you're balancing school and your activities? How are things going with your friends? Is there anything that's bothering you at home or at school? And then let your child's answer give you information for any potential followup.

Letting your child know that weight gain during puberty (around 40 pounds) is completely normal and natural is really important, too. Changing hormones and the fact that, for females assigned at birth, the body needs to be able to hold onto extra fat in order to eventually be ready to carry a child if she chooses. Puberty is a crucial point where many, girls especially, feel uncomfortable with their changing and growing bodies. They may want to cling to their childhood body and fear looking different if they go through puberty before their friends. Being the "only one" to change can be challenging, and I encourage you to find ways to help support your child.

Give your child plenty of support and positive feedback that these body changes might feel scary, but it's also exciting, and never, never criticize, shame, or call unnecessary attention to changing bodies. Remind your child that every body is unique and teach them the right way to care for their body. Emphasizing the importance of eating foods that taste good, going to school, getting enough sleep, moving their bodies, making friends, spending time in nature, and finding ways to decrease their stress, like journaling or yoga, will all contribute to their overall happiness. These are some of the concrete things we can teach our kids to help them feel good. Reiterate that anything related to food and movement should be done through a weight-neutral lens and never with the goal of trying to change or control their bodies because everyone's body size is largely beyond their control no matter what other people outside of your home say.

Remind your kid that all bodies are good bodies and that they're loved unconditionally. Keep talking to your sons and daughters during this important time. While your child is growing, they still need you as a guide, even if they push you away. Gaining independence is a necessary part of their individuation to eventually have their own identity and function on their own. Once our babies leave the womb or our arms, it's a slow rollercoaster ride teaching, nurturing, loving, guiding, encouraging, being challenged, and letting go, even though our natural tendency may be to pack their lunch and put on their Band-Aids forever.

While you're giving your kid compliments, soak up some of the same advice for yourself. You're loved unconditionally, and it's okay and normal for your body to change at various times in your life, too. Our bodies aren't meant to look the same way decade after decade.

* * *

SUMMARY

Kids' bodies are meant to change during puberty. Somehow this message has been missed, but it's very normal for kids to gain around 40 pounds during this time. Talking with your doctor (without your child present) about any sudden weight loss or weight gain changes can be helpful if you're worried there might be a bigger problem. It's important to let your kid know that you love and support them unconditionally, and you think they're beautiful no matter what. Even a comment that might seem like a compliment can come back later to haunt a kid whose body is changing. Never ever participate in body shaming toward your kid, and while you're at it, follow the same advice for yourself!

* * *

MANTRA

- I will not comment on my child's body size.
- I will treat myself and my kid with kindness when I experience body changes.
- I will choose the attitude "this is what I've got" when it comes to my body, and I'm going to treat it with care.

Give Your Kid Non-Body Compliments

My daughter had just put on her sparkly rainbow skirt that doubled as a tutu, her older sister had fixed her hair into perfect little pigtails and purple bows, and she was proudly displaying her sequined-heart shirt. In those moments, it's hard for me not to gush and say, "Look at you; you're so beautiful. You look absolutely adorable!"

I used to think it was my duty to pile on the praise like an ice cream sundae layered with chocolate sauce, bananas, jimmies, and cherries. I thought this was especially true for my girls so they'd never, for a minute, doubt their beauty, confidence, or worth. Little did I know that the extra praise I was dishing might actually cause them more harm than good.

The irony here is the more you focus on your child's appearance, the more they'll assign their worth to their appearance. Research has shown that kids as young as 3 years old can have body image issues. Even the way you express your feelings through your body language can teach kids that bodies must be perfect and that they'll need to do anything to achieve perfection to ensure their happiness, love, worth, acceptance, and admiration from others. There's a reason the diet industry rakes in over $70 billion dollars a year, and of that number, $16 billion can be attributed to cosmetic plastic surgery procedures.

I want our kids to know how much I absolutely adore and love them, and I think there's a balanced way to let kids know their value beyond appearance. My goal is to give fewer body-related comments across the board and mostly give compliments that highlight my child's character and strengthen our connection. For example, you can say to your child, "Aww, you look so pretty in that dress!" And then follow up the comment with something about their character, like, "I love how you took responsibility and got ready by yourself!" Or you can choose to say, "I love how you put that outfit together. Tell me about how you chose those colors." This gets at the child's personality and character more than just an outward appearance comment.

Another thing I make a point to do is to tell our kids that they look beautiful whether they're wearing pajamas or their Sunday best. I purposefully let them know how much I enjoy their company when we're on vacation and when we're sitting home reading a book. I truly believe all kids are interesting and have so much to say. When I meet a new child or our kids have friends over to the house, I like to have a few questions at the ready. I get down to their level and interact with them instead of just saying to the parent, "Oh my gosh, your kid is so cute!" Here are a few of my favorites:

"What's one of your favorite books?"

"What's your favorite sport or activity?"

"What's your favorite thing to do outside?"

"Do you have a favorite food?"

"Where's your favorite place to visit?"

But what happens when your kid comes to you with the age-old question, "Am I pretty?" You absolutely can answer, "Yes, you're beautiful in so many ways." You can mention a couple of physical characteristics, like, "I love your eyes, your face, and your arms for hugging." And you can also mention all the characteristics inside them that you love, like their strength, determination, and resilience. You can touch on things that your kid enjoys doing, like, "You're a beautiful dancer or strong athlete or talented singer." The idea is that you want your kid to know that beauty isn't just skin deep. Beauty, like health, isn't a black and white topic, and you can decide your own definition of beauty instead of accepting diet culture's unrealistic, almost impossible-to-reach-without-plastic-surgery Barbie doll standards.

I make it a point to say nice things now and then about my body in front of our kids but never focus on appearance. The more I focus on their character and not their appearance determining their worth or value, the better. I absolutely make it a point to look in the mirror and not pick, poke, sigh in disgust, or say that I look terrible. Yes, I enjoy taking care of myself, but I tend to emphasize the deeper qualities about myself and them as the default. Teaching our kids to prize their appearance is a losing battle since, as far as I can see, wrinkles happen and body parts change. There is no Benjamin Button aging-in-reverse, despite the beauty industry using some of the same empty promise tactics as the diet industry. How many times have you bought the miracle cream that promises to "stop" aging in its tracks?

Remember, our girls are absorbing more than we realize. In a survey from KidsHealth, 90% of girls said their moms were pretty, and the feeling was mutual for moms and their girls. Unfortunately, only 41% of girls thought they themselves were pretty, and 50% of both moms and daughters say they dislike how they look in a selfie. 40% of moms thought they weren't beautiful, and of those, 76% complained aloud to their daughter about needing to lose weight. Ouch, this is certainly not the messaging we want our kids absorbing at home.

The only thing we need to lose is the overimportance placed on appearance from birth. If I had a dollar for every time I got unsolicited information about our baby's body size (he's so chubby, I love those rolls, she's so tiny), I'd be buying a ticket for the next SpaceX mission to outer space. Except I won't ever do that because I get horrible motion sickness and that would be my nightmare.

Let's make our earthly mission to change the conversation within ourselves first and then shift our focus for our kids, too. The bottom line is we want our kids and other kids to know that their appearance isn't the first thing we see or what we're focused on. We want them to know that character counts and we love and value them no matter their outward appearance.

* * *

Summary

Our society places immense value on a person's appearance. Instead of focusing all your attention on your or your child's appearance, what would it feel like to focus on their characteristics instead? What would it feel like to let your kid know how much they're valued and appreciated regardless of their looks? Who would you become if you focused less on your wrinkles and more on your wish list for life? How would your kid benefit from hearing about what you like about their character instead of their clothing? See what happens when you devalue outward characteristics and place a higher value on what you and your kid can do and what you want to be or how you want to be remembered. "Here lies Susie, with her great breasts and butt," said nobody's tombstone ever.

* * *

Mantra

- I will make a point to give my kid non-body-related compliments.
- I can see the beauty in my kids beyond their appearance.
- I have many ways to show my kids how much I love them that have nothing to do with commenting on their size.

Handling Bad Body Image Days (BBIDs)

I was in my happy place snuggled up next to my daughter with a book when she said something that hit me in the pit of my stomach. My sweet girl looked down at her legs next to mine and said, "My legs are too big."

It took everything in my power not to shout, "That's complete crap, and diet culture sucks, and you're beautiful and perfect just the way you are, so don't ever think that thought for one more second, ok?!" But I refrained and said this instead: "You're not feeling good about your legs today? Can you please tell me why?"

"Well, they're just big."

Luckily I had my bigger legs right next to hers for reference, and I said, "Well does that mean my legs are too big?"

She giggled and said, "No, Mommy, yours are good."

This realization led us to a conversation about what big or small even means and who gets to determine that. Once she felt like she'd uncovered some tough moments from her day that had nothing to do with her legs, we were able to get back to books and snuggles, but I wasn't even for a second considering that this was a one-and-done conversation. Nope, this was going to be a regular conversation because she's female, because she's growing up in a diet culture world, and because unrealistic images are constantly thrown your, my, and my daughter's way every hour of the day.

What do you do when you're having a "bad body image day" (BBID)? These days happen for all humans, especially recovering dieters and pre-teens/teens who might be struggling with their changing bodies.

We're told if we're thin, everything will be coming up rainbows and daisies. So, if we aren't feeling happy and magical, it's easy to see how we turn feelings of fear and anxiety about our life into our body size and "fat" feelings. We're taught our size can be changed or managed, even though this is only true for a tiny fraction of the population. Focusing our energy and attention on our size is our way of managing something that feels "bad" or uncontrollable.

Where does body image even come from? Summer Innanen, coach, author, and podcaster, teaches that societal oppressions and psychosocial factors drive body image. Societal pressures like sexism, racism, ageism, ableism, along with the belief that you'll never be good enough, strongly affect body image. The amount of value that people derive from their appearance is another indicator of body image, along with how much time they spend negatively thinking about their bodies.

So, what do you really mean when you say, "I feel fat?" This is usually code for: "I'm feeling any number of uncomfortable feelings, like nervousness, fear, anxiety, or insecurity." When you or your kid say the word fat, remember that it's a description and not a feeling, and there's usually a feeling to uncover.

A feeling is different from your physical reality. In order to figure out your feelings, you have to dig deep, like a sea diver looking for lost treasure, to find out what those "fat" feelings are really trying to tell you. If you notice that you're going about your life not really thinking about your body and then, bam, "fat" feelings suddenly arise, I encourage you to think about what's changed in your life. What might be the root cause of these feelings? If it's fear you feel, what might be triggering your sense of fear? What feels outside of your control that's scary? Are you feeling anxious about something happening in your life? Once you uncover your true feelings, you can work on processing and managing them. This is a much safer approach than dieting, which will likely cause further emotional and physical harm and won't address the root cause of your discomfort.

Why do we even care about our bodies in the first place? We only care about the fat on our body because of what we (thanks to our societal brainwashing) make it mean. Diet culture, our friends, and family have very likely associated fat with a long list of negative attributes that we still believe to be true. Knowing that these feelings are very normal and that it's not a matter of if, but when, they arise, what can you do?

Once you notice you're having a BBID, see if you can sit with discomfort first instead of making a plan for the next diet, the next elimination or cleanse, or the next crazy workout schedule. You deserve to give your feelings attention and not attempt to ease your anxiety or fear through dieting. In fact, many anti-diet coaches believe that dieting is the real addiction we all need to quit.

When sitting with discomfort, ask yourself, "If I'm not feeling fat, what am I feeling?" Continue the inquiry with, "If I wasn't obsessing about my body right now…"

1. What would I be thinking about instead? (A difficult conversation with a loved one, a stressful situation with my kids, not getting "enough" done in my day?)
2. What would I be dealing with in my life right now? (An illness, overwhelm, exhaustion, anxiousness about an upcoming event?)

As other feelings arise, notice, name, and try locating them in your body. Where is this feeling in your body? What does it feel like? What does it look like? What might these sensations be trying to tell you? Breathe into these feelings and try visualizing them as a part. Ask that feeling/part what they need and what they're trying to tell you. This language I'm referencing with feelings as parts comes from Dr. Richard Schwartz's IFS (Internal Family Systems) model. I'm not an expert in this field, but I encourage you to look into this system of healing if it speaks to you. However, it's not necessary to know any more than what I shared here. Simply having awareness of a feeling, finding its body location, and trying to sit with it is very helpful.

This plan for examining your feelings beyond feeling "fat" for yourself might sound doable, but what about other people's opinions of you (which you can't and never will be able to control), which often trigger BBIDs?

Know that no matter what, people will judge. You can be the juiciest peach, and if someone doesn't like a peach, they aren't going to be into you. It's okay, they're just not your people, and you're not their people. We simply can't be everything to everybody. Other people's opinions are really just a reflection of their likes, dislikes, and opinions, and nothing factual about you. And, besides, people are really so busy dealing with things going on in their own lives that they're noticing details about us much less than we think. Remind yourself that people of all sizes find meaningful relationships, get married, have children, buy houses, pursue great careers, find ways to give back to society and their community, and so much more.

What if you simply committed to believing in your own beauty? Beauty is subjective, so don't wait for others to label you beautiful. Why wait when you have the power to do this for yourself? You really can create whatever truth you want. Nobody can take that away from you!

Keep committing to continual surrender and acceptance and

taking the best care of yourself in any given moment, and what other people say will matter less and less. Loving yourself all the time or constantly feeling like Mary Poppins isn't a requirement to having good body image. Instead, your goal over time is to be able to accept and appreciate your body regardless of size or appearance. You don't have to love your body every second of every day.

While your BBIDs will likely never be zero, the way you approach these days is key. The real secret is that you don't have to love your body and can still be committed to treating your body with respect, which means you won't participate in diet culture's punishing ways that can harm you both physically and mentally. Since dieting isn't a viable option, what else can you do to feel good? As Sheryl Sandberg's book suggests, what's your Option B? What other values can you focus on or tap into that have nothing to do with your body size?

One more tool to combating BBIDs is finding a better thought when you notice negative thinking. Have you ever said these things to yourself? Or what if your kid starts saying these things?

"I'm so fat."

"My stomach is disgusting."

"Nobody is going to love me."

"I hate how I look."

If your kid is in a larger body and says they feel "fat," you may want to say, "Yes, you do have a larger body." You can explain that it can be really hard to have a larger body because other kids say mean things and that people assume all sorts of negative things about larger-bodied people (fat stigma), which is all too common in our unfortunately fatphobic world. It's important to make sure your kid feels supported, has strategies in place for different scenarios, and knows that weight loss or attempting to alter their body size isn't a viable or safe option. If your kid has this same comment but is thin, ask your kid what it means when they say fat. Try to tease out what else they might be feeling and help them get to the root of their concerns.

If you're the one making these comments, try this strategy. First, identify the thought behind your feeling. Once you can identify the thought that brought up these "fat" feelings, ask yourself if that's a thought you want to keep or if you'd like to change your thought and repeat something else in your head when BBIDs happen.

You could try going to rainbows and daisies right away with these positive affirmations:

"My body is perfect."

"My stomach is awesome."

"I'm going to find my dream partner next week!"

BUT, going from zero to 60 rarely works and often fails in the short, if not long, term.

I suggest finding a neutral thought instead. The key is this neutral thought must be believable in order to slowly change the wiring in your brain over time. Right now, you likely have some thoughts that have been repeated so often that they flow like a six-lane highway in your brain. Your neutral thought will likely feel like a bumpy back road instead of your smooth highway. The thought is new and feels awkward, and that's normal.

"I have a body."

"Other people besides me have a stomach that looks like this."

"People all over the world of all shapes and sizes find partners."

"This is the body I live in."

"I want to treat my body well."

Once you believe this thought over time, you can pick another thought that has a more positive feel.

"My body is worthy."

"My stomach is a vital part of my being and serves me daily."

"There's someone I can have a great relationship with."

A final tool you may want to try with self-talk comes from author

Ethan Kross, who wrote the book, *Chatter*. Consider using what he refers to as distanced self-talk. Using your name first followed by the advice you might give to a friend in the same situation or the advice you need to hear can be very effective. "Molly, you can find ways to appreciate your body. You can find the strength to help yourself and others find peace and acceptance." Notice the use of the word "you" instead of "I" as a means to maintain this distanced self-talk.

If you think you're alone when it comes to body image, think again. Give yourself compassion for having such strong feelings about your body. Offer loving-kindness to yourself and understanding. Remind yourself that all humans suffer, and the suffering you feel is likely felt by others. All human beings have strengths and weaknesses, both real and perceived. Remind yourself that you don't have to believe everything you think. You can choose what you want to focus on, even if it doesn't seem that way.

When you notice a moment of self-criticism, ask yourself what the most supportive message would be to yourself instead. If we want to motivate ourselves, love is always more powerful than fear. Self-compassion is always more powerful than self-criticism. Kristin Neff teaches that "unlike self-criticism, which asks if you're good enough, self-compassion asks what's good for you." We can literally flood our bodies with oxytocin from love or douse our system with cortisol when our brain (amygdala) goes into overdrive.

Ask yourself what you need right now. A few minutes alone, time to rest, a phone call to a friend, time to write in a journal, time to get angry at a system of oppression that includes fatphobia and weight stigma?

It's also important to examine some common BBID triggers. A very common trigger is clothing. If too tight clothes triggered you into your BBID, I highly recommend doing a closet clean out and getting rid of any clothing that doesn't fit. It's perfectly fine to keep clothes that fall within your body's natural weight range so you have options of comfort within a size up or down. The problem comes when many people struggle with letting go of their "skinny" clothes as it feels like a form of giving up on a dream. I want to assure you that accepting your body right now is never a sign of giving up. It's a sign of strength. If you're still struggling to toss items, you can box up clothes that are too hard to part with and leave them tucked away and decide over time when you're ready to let go. Removing immediate triggers is a great first step in showing your body that it deserves clothing that fits and feels good.

Notice that I purposely avoid using the term "clothes that flatter" your body, which really means clothes that make you look thinner. Choose clothes based on style and comfort, but not because they make you look thin. No need to fuel diet culture's mentality in your sacred closet space where you start and end your day.

Wouldn't it be great if body image wasn't even a thing? Can you imagine waking up with no concept of body image and asking yourself, what would I do with my day? How would I dress? How would I talk with people? What wouldn't I do in the name of diet culture? How would this change how you act and feel in your life? I encourage you to write down the answers to these important questions.

And remember, compassion, curiosity, and kindness are always an option and ultimately the way out of pain. Tomorrow is a new day. What do you want to think on purpose about your body?

* * *

SUMMARY

BBIDs are (almost) inevitable. Bad body moments, hours, and days will happen. We live in a diet-obsessed culture, and the messages are oftentimes hard to ignore. Kindness and compassion are always the best choices during these difficult times, along with being willing to see what's happening on a deeper level. Our body doesn't change minute to minute or hour to hour, but our thinking does change. We tend to turn toward trying to "fix" our bodies during times of stress, duress, anxiety, or fear. Remind yourself that your body is not the problem and ask yourself what else could be the problem? Remind yourself that you're committed to not "fixing" yourself, and find thoughts or phrases that you can repeat to yourself when these BBID attacks occur. Honor your body and the space you occupy in the world. Loving your body isn't a requirement, but respecting and accepting your body is necessary.

* * *

MANTRA

- I will choose kindness, compassion, and grace when I have a bad body image day attack.
- My body can do incredible things and deserves respect and to be cared for. My body is where I live. It's my home that I want to care for.
- My body is never the problem. There is beauty in all bodies.

Section 4

Common Parenting Pitfalls

Encourage Excitement, Involvement, and Exploration with Food

One of my favorite pictures of my girls is a photo of them running with a friend, all three clad in rain boots and sweatshirts with fresh face tattoos from the face painting booth. They had their right arms held high, fists grasping fresh kale and Swiss chard picked from the farm. Slide Ranch in the Bay Area was the perfect place to explore the farm, gorgeous coastal trails, and tide pools.

At the time, we were living in San Francisco, a food lover's and eco-conscious consumer's dream. The preschool my daughter attended had daily gardening chores, so each child had a hand in tending the garden goodies. Parents and kids alike would delight in the daily harvest. From an early age, we tried to show our kids that food was fun and something to be excited about.

Equally as fun as the garden are trips to Nana's house where the kids are always invited to join in cooking whatever is on for dinner. Holidays are extra special as their nana lets them in on cooking secrets and involves them in making delicious pans of baked pasta, Christmas cookies that melt in your mouth, and crisp salads with the perfect vinaigrette dressing.

Food is fun, and kids generally LOVE learning about how food grows, where it comes from, and how to cook. Involving your child from the very beginning is a great way to let kids know that food is not only fun but safe. When kids feel safe around food, they're much more likely to be adventurous and try new things.

Even the littlest kids can get involved with dinner preparation by taking food out of packages, pouring water, rinsing off fruit or vegetables, breaking up food, shaking up a dressing, or sprinkling toppings on salads, pastas, or ice cream. Older kids can help with cutting, stirring, setting the table, tasting (who doesn't love that first noodle taste?), and measuring ingredients (a free math lesson on the side, too!). Getting our kids to learn basic cooking is an important life skill. For our teen and tween, I often tell them that YOYO (you're on your own) for lunch or breakfast, and I'm usually impressed with what they come up with.

It's also important to let there be an element of play when it comes to food and your kids. Imagine that an alien has just landed on Planet Earth for the first time and is looking at what you've served for dinner. So many colors, textures, shapes, and flavors! Your little alien friend might not be too keen to jump right in. Instead of trying to convince your alien that these foods are good and delicious and good for you, you might try finding a friendly alien food (buttered noodles) and let your alien get involved with the other foods in any way they'd like to. Maybe your alien friend wants to look at, smell, and touch the food on their plate. Maybe your friend would like to assess the situation from afar. Maybe your alien decides to take a bite (no need to force a no-thank-you bite, which means you *have* to try one bite) but then spits it out immediately. That's all part of your new friend's process and totally okay.

You can't know what your alien's tastes are, so there's no point in forcing, blaming, or shaming, no matter how hard you worked to plan for the alien's first earthly dinner. Standing next to your alien friend and breathing down their neck with anxious anticipation about their next bite probably isn't the best approach either. You might even want to let the alien know that you can see there are a lot of new things and assure the alien that they'll know when they're ready to try something new. Next time the alien might even want to help you cook before their spaceship goes back to outer space and the alien brings you to their house for a plate of all new foods. Imagine how you'd feel in this scenario, and see if that doesn't help remove a little mealtime stress.

Allowing your kid to be playful around food helps them have a completely different attitude than another kid who might be forced to eat something.

Give your child space and time to explore, and get your kids involved early and often!

* * *

SUMMARY

Food is fun! Find ways big and small that you can involve your kids in growing, preparing, and cooking food. Even the smallest eaters can get involved! It's important to give kids space to explore their food in a no-pressure/no-guilt zone, so they feel safe. Adopting a playful versus punishing strategy around food is recommended. No-thank-you bites or other forms of coercion can put too much pressure on kids and create negative associations with food. Imagine what an alien friend might feel like when they see and taste food for the first time!

* * *

- I will get my kids involved with food when I can.
- I will give my child space to explore food and not take their food choices personally.
- What my child eats isn't a reflection of my parenting.

Rethink Food as a Reward

Sweat dripped from my chest as I leaned forward in the plastic lawn chair to get the best view of my daughter's swim lessons. San Francisco's fall wind whipped up the leaves outside, but inside it was a sauna. In the lane next to my daughter, a little boy refused to participate in his lesson. He sat quietly on the side while his mom tried coaxing him into the water. After an unsuccessful pitch, the mom handed her son over to the instructor, who looked ready for battle with his kickboard. The boy was having none of it. His mom was clearly at the end of her trick book when she finally snapped, "Okay! You can have any food you want at the store, aaaannnnd I'll let you have a popsicle or ice cream if you do your swim lesson!!"

What parent hasn't been in these shoes? The "I'll do anything to get you to cooperate shoes!"I get it. You just want your kid to listen and *do what they are supposed to do* and stop embarrassing you, and offering sugar as the reward works because many parents withhold sugar from their kids for various reasons. I've been that desperate mom in many locations—grocery stores, church, Target, swimming pools, and kids' classes. I absolutely used to offer food as a reward before I learned how damaging that could be to a child's relationship with food and their emotional well-being.

When I find myself in those difficult situations where I'd prefer to escape through a trap door in the floor, I always like to ask myself, "Okay, what's really going on here?" "I wonder what my child might be thinking or feeling." When my child is dysregulated (aka having a tantrum), my first approach is to name what they're feeling and why. *Are you feeling nervous about swimming because Mom won't be in the water with you?* Attempting to open up a conversation about what your child is experiencing is a way for them to feel seen and heard. Trying to find a way to connect with your kid is key. In order to move forward to the problem-solving stage with my kid, I need to have made a connection with them at an emotional level first.

Offering food as a way to reward your child is problematic in a couple of ways. First, offering food as a solution doesn't get to the root of the problem. Why was your child feeling dysregulated in the first place? Acknowledging your child's emotional experience is so important. By doing this, you show your child that you care and that you want to understand and connect with them. Letting your kid know that their feelings are seen and heard and allowed is so important.

The other problem with food as a reward is that it teaches kids on some level that food needs to be earned. Your kid might start to believe that they need to perform a certain way in order to eat certain foods. They may also think that they need to demonstrate their worth or value in order to eat something. Neither message is one we want our kids to internalize.

Let's set the record straight on this one. As Dana Sturtevant and Hilary Kinavy, founders of The Center for Body Trust, say, body trust is every person's birthright. That trust includes your ability to eat food in response to your body's needs, not because it had to be earned. There's no behavior you need to demonstrate to determine your worth, which, in my humble opinion, is 100% at birth. Do you want to enjoy ice cream just because? Great! Your child doesn't need a straight-A report card to earn any kind of food.

Instead of relying on food to get your child to do what you want, open up a conversation about what might be going on for your child. Use natural consequences that aren't threats. "If you don't get in the pool, I'm going to take away your screen time for the week" are two unrelated activities that will be hard for your child to make an association with. Instead, you may ask your child if there's any portion of the lesson that they're comfortable with. Is there a part of you that wants to get in, but another part of you wants to stay out of the pool? What do they want? If they want you to teach the lesson, you can empathize and say that you know it's hard that you can't be the teacher, but you're going to be right here cheering them on when they feel comfortable getting in the water. Or offer that there's something about doing something with someone you don't know very well that can feel a little scary. You might say to your kid that if they don't get in the water, they can choose to sit and watch the lesson instead. Maybe next week, they'll want to sit and watch with their toes in the water, or maybe you'll decide that it's best to retry the lesson at a later date.

Oftentimes, we need to check in with our own thoughts and feelings about situations involving our kids and remind ourselves that nothing has gone wrong here and that we're doing our best. Leave food out of your reward and consequences conversations, and your kid won't feel pressure to behave in any way in order to get food they want and deserve.

A final note and parenting pro tip is to make sure your kid is well-fed throughout the day so they have enough energy to tackle their daily activities. Nobody feels or does well on an empty stomach.

Summary

Tying food to behavior can leave a child feeling like they don't "deserve" certain foods if they don't demonstrate perfect behavior or they're "bad" if they do eat certain foods labeled as a "treat" for no reason other than it's noon on a Wednesday. Using food as a way to solve your child's problem doesn't address the root issue they're having. If you can make an emotional connection, you might stop feeling desperate for a solution because, let's face it, many of our kid's problems don't need a solution outside of empathy or being able to sit with discomfort. Repeat after me: "Food is not a reward." Food is necessary for life, and you and your kid can choose what you want to eat for whatever reason or no reason at all! I recommend that you stop labeling and using food as treats or rewards and allow yourself and your kid to eat sweet food just because it's delicious.

* * *

Mantra

- I am deserving of food because I'm alive.
- My child or I never have to earn the food that we want to eat.
- Food isn't a reward for behavior, and a lack of food isn't a punishment for behavior.

Call Foods What They Are

I'll never forget when my son, at age two, said the word penis at a playdate. A couple of friends tried to stifle their laughter, and another one said, "Oh, so you just call it what it is?"

With a slight hesitation in my voice, I said, "Ummm, yeah. We just call it as we see it at our house."

Pee-pee, wee-wee, jayjay, peeny, ginah are all creative and interesting terms for private parts, but they don't help parents lay the important groundwork to be able to talk about sex and sexuality in an open and honest way. And those made-up words can indicate to a kid that their private parts are shameful in some way. Our bodies are normal and amazing, so calling our body parts what they are and teaching our children their correct names can help remove any shame, guilt, or fear that might otherwise develop by having code names. It's not the who-ha, schmoobie, or ding-ding. It's vagina, breast, and penis.

Just like we want to teach our kids to call a vagina a vagina, we also want to teach our kids to call foods by their name. Have you ever picked up your kid from school or celebrated a sporting event win by asking if they want to get a "treat?" I know this seems rather harmless, but labeling foods other than what they are puts them into a category that can have many connotations. Does treat mean something negative because you think they really aren't "good" for you? Do treats mean that you have to earn them based on certain behavior? Do treats mean that your kid only deserves them after they've earned them through good grades? Does getting a treat mean that this food is "special" in some way and only to be enjoyed on rare occasions?

We want to call foods what they are, too. Instead of a reward, treat, or dessert, try these phrases: Let's go get ice cream. Do you want to have a cookie? Do you want to have some chocolate after dinner? Do you want to have a lollipop while we wait in line?

If you're offering your child a tasty item, just ask them if they want that particular food. This way, there are no strings attached, no hierarchy of foods, just an offering of food that can be enjoyed anytime you want them. Let's learn to call things what they are across the board.

* * *

Summary

While it's tempting to put foods in broad categories like desserts or treats, it's best to just call foods what they are, just like we teach our kids to call their body parts by their correct scientific name. By labeling foods as treats, we inadvertently put foods into categories with hierarchy. You or your kid might start to believe that they can only eat these foods if they do well at school, do their chores, eat all their dinner, win the soccer game, or earn the item through any form of work or achievement. Food is our birthright, not something we have to earn in any way. Food is meant to be a neutral offering, enjoyed anytime we need or want to eat and enjoy it.

MANTRA

- I will commit to calling foods what they are and not use broad categories to label foods.
- I will not refer to food as a treat because eating any kind of food is everyone's birthright.
- I will not pressure myself or my kids to feel as though they need to earn the right to eat certain foods or punish them for eating any foods.

Stop Labeling Foods as Good, Bad, Junk, or Fuel

"You're so emo!" shouted one of our kids as one of their siblings threw their toy car across the room.

"What does that even mean?!" I asked.

"Duh, Mom, everyone uses that word for the kids who dress in black clothes, have black hair, and are overly emotional."

Overly emotional kid? Check. There's no denying that we have some highly sensitive kids at our house. But using this label sends the overly emotional kid into an even deeper emotional rut. The word "emo" isn't allowed in our house anymore because labeling anyone with this term doesn't have a positive connotation, causes further harm, and actually doesn't give an accurate description of the situation or person it's supposedly describing.

The truth is the labels we put on people and things matter. Words like "designer," "luxury," and "bespoke" automatically mean more expensive. Words like "jock," "trendsetter," or "cool" can put you straight in the popular crowd. Words like "weirdo," "emo," or "different" can land kids in the not-so-popular groups, while "knockoff," "imitation," or "dupe" will have you searching for anything with a .99

ending. Our words constantly shape our opinions, thoughts, and beliefs about the people and things in the world around us, and labeling foods in a certain way is no different.

The diet industry knows that labels matter and give certain foods a "bad" name or demonizes them in order to promote their product, plan, or cleanse. Anything you consider bad or wrong will ignite your fear, which motivates you to invest in something "better," which just so happens to support diet culture and the weight loss industry. Fat, sugar, cholesterol, processed, refined, gluten, carbs, and fiber are just a few of the buzzwords that decorate the front of almost every food box or can. Diet culture especially likes to demonize certain foods (fat, cholesterol, sugar) while other foods are elevated (vegetables, gluten-free, sugar-free foods). It should come as no surprise that these elevated foods are often double, triple or quadruple the price of their "regular" counterparts, yet nutritionally, these foods are nearly identical.

Food has been given enormous power in terms of its contribution to our health, but the reality is that food and exercise *together* account for only 20% or less of your overall health. The largest contributors to your health are the social determinants of health, which includes genetics, socioeconomic status, your environment, the amount of discrimination you experience, and other factors that are largely outside of your control. The truth is that certain foods or food groups aren't inherently bad, but our thoughts about foods can be so powerful that we can see physical effects in our bodies regardless of the validity of our thoughts. Having three to five servings of fruits and vegetables throughout the day can positively impact health, but eating copious amounts of vegetables isn't necessary to achieve healthy superhero building-jumping invincibility status.

Have you ever read an article in a magazine about how gluten can cause bloating and then, OMG, you're a full believer that, yes, indeed, gluten does cause bloating? The "experts" in the article confirmed it's true. Regardless of gluten actually causing bloating physiologically, your staunch belief will actually be powerful enough to give your body the physical experience of bloating. This medical phenomenon is called the nocebo effect. Maybe you feel tired and immediately blame wheat instead of looking at whether you're getting enough sleep, eating enough food, running around after toddlers, or going through a stressful experience.

If you're so busy labeling foods, you'll be disconnecting from what it is you really want and desire, which usually leads to restriction and eventually eating more food down the road. How many times have you eschewed the pasta primavera for a salad at the restaurant only to find yourself staring down the pantry at 10 p.m. because you're still starving? Or maybe you skipped the cake at the birthday party but ended up elbow deep in a row of Oreos later on. When you worry about and label food as good and bad, it might prevent you from eating something short term, but the long-term effect is that restriction will increase binge eating episodes.

I also hear people constantly talking about how they only eat food for fuel and don't eat or want their kids to eat "junk." Eating food for fuel alone is akin to only having sex for the purpose of having a baby. Food is meant for more than just providing us with the energy needed to get through our days. It's meant to bring us pleasure and provide joy so that we're inclined to keep giving our body the energy it needs. If food didn't provide any joy, nobody would be drawn to eat, and none of us would survive!

Our survival is rooted in receiving the basic building blocks (aka macronutrients) from a variety of foods. Some foods are higher in carbohydrates; other foods are higher in fat; other foods are higher in protein; and others are higher in fiber. And some foods are composed of primarily one macronutrient. Listening to your body will help you find the right foods you need at the right time, and you don't need to worry about labeling your food as anything other than food.

The same holds true for allowing your kids to decide what and how much they want from what you serve and giving them some flexibility to choose their own snacks when it's age-appropriate. Shaming a child around food can disrupt their trust in themselves and what they know is best for their body. It's not uncommon for children to be naturally drawn to high-density/energy foods or have a narrow food palate for a prolonged period of time. If you have a toddler or school-aged child, chances are you've seen your child literally run, jump, hop, or skip through the day and end the day with running races down the hallway. The massive growth changes they're going through mean they need a lot of energy and are often drawn to get their needs met through high-density foods that are easily digestible—hello, bread with butter!

Avoid labeling the food your kids eat as bad or unhealthy, and simply continue to offer a variety of foods. The old phrase "you are what you eat" doesn't account for the fact that we truly are much more than what we put on our plate. Our emotional health that's fueled through connection, relationships, pleasure, and joy contributes a great deal to our overall health and wellness and can't be served up from a diet-focused plan or measured out in half-cup servings. Food isn't the only way to health and, in fact, is a small portion (pun intended) of the bigger picture of a balanced life.

* * *

SUMMARY

I encourage you to stop labeling your food as anything other than food. The more you can think and talk about your food in a neutral way, the better. Diet culture has villainized many of our foods, and it's time to strip the good, bad, junk, and other negative connotations associated with our food so we can listen to our innate wisdom and make choices from a place of neutrality, not from a place of should, guilt, shame, or fear. Food and exercise have been given power as the ultimate tools to achieve health, and it's simply not true. Social determinants of health play a much larger role when it comes to wellness. Emotional health is also key to our overall health, and spending countless hours a day obsessing about food and exercise will negatively affect your emotional well-being. Finding peace with food is worth the effort so you can enjoy life on a much deeper level.

* * *

MANTRA

- I will view all foods neutrally.
- I will know that foods have different nutritional values and that choosing to eat different foods at different times based on my emotional and physical needs is valid.
- I will teach my kids that food doesn't belong in categories like junk, good, bad, fuel, or filler. Food is food, and it all can have a place on our table.

Ditch the Clean Plate Club and Food Comments

My dad always had a goofy joke to tell at the dinner table. I think he knew it was his best tactic for keeping his two girls smiling and laughing, which made us that much more likely to actually talk about our day at school instead of giving the standard "fine" answer to every question.

"Don't forget to eat every carrot and pea on your plate, but don't really pee on your plate!"

"I wonder what vegetables are in this soup? Do you think there are some potatoes? Maybe we should take a peek, I mean take a leek!"

Even my father-in-law had a favorite joke about the honeymoon salad, which was "lettuce alone," or his other fan favorite, "We're having chicken for dinner, wanna neck?"

My dad was head of the dad bad jokes club, so it's no surprise that he would show off his clean plate at the end of his meal and say, "Who else wants to be part of The Clean Plate Club?" I can remember his silly grin as he showed me his clean plate and boasted that he was a proud member of this exciting club. The club didn't hold meaning in our house in that he never forced us to eat a certain amount of food. It was simply something "fun" that my dad liked to joke about.

Unfortunately, many parents tell their children that they have to clean their plate in order to get dessert or they have to try this food or eat that vegetable in order to get more of a different food, like bread or pasta. If that doesn't work, another popular tactic is to remind kids that there are starving children all over the world who would be grateful to have a nice warm meal. Once again, using guilt and shame to make you or your child change is an ineffective strategy.

Growing kids and adults have tastes and hunger levels that are constantly changing. Ever notice that some days you feel ravenous and want just about anything in sight and other days you just peck at your food like a bird who'd rather fly? Our body is a miraculous being able to accurately tell us through our hunger and satiety cues how much we need each day to maintain our weight set point (WSP). The programming in our body is better than anything Steve Jobs or any Apple brainiac could ever dream of inventing.

Our WSP is unique to each of us, and our body will fight hard to keep us in a range that fluctuates between 5 and 20 pounds. This is, of course, if we aren't messing with our intake by purposely trying to reduce our body size through restriction or eating a lot more than what our body needs. Staying in our WSP range happens automatically by miraculous measures that are simply incomprehensible to the thinking brain. It's incredibly difficult to stay below or go above our set point range and it's not possible to permanently alter your innate set point range. WSPs can change throughout the course of your life, too. It's important to know dieting can bump up your WSP in order to protect your body from dipping below its set point again. A first dieting attempt can seem relatively easy, but each subsequent diet is faced at a higher set point, making weight loss even more difficult. Set points very often go up and very rarely go down.

Besides changing hunger needs from day to day, encouraging your kid to eat above or below a level that overrides their body's internal satiety cues teaches your kid that they shouldn't trust their inner voice or their body's instincts around food. Kids of all ages need to develop a relationship of trust with their bodies in order to feel safe and comfortable in their own skin.

One more important reason to skip the clean plate club is that forcing your kid to eat foods they don't want to eat can provide a negative association with that food. Food is meant to bring us pleasure and joy, and being forced to eat something you don't like leaves a lasting impression and can even turn a child off from eating certain foods indefinitely. I have a childhood friend who could barely stomach scrambled eggs because she associated it with her stepmom forcing her to eat them before she could go outside to play. Food can be a powerful association to a negative situation or experience.

Finally, trying to guilt a kid into eating food that could otherwise have gone to a kid in need is a form of shame and guilt that could also lead to problematic eating behaviors. If a kid learns to eat because they feel guilty, this is also disconnecting them from their inner wisdom. Guilt might work to get your kid to wear that ugly Christmas sweater from Aunt Susie, but guilt and shame have no place when it comes to any behaviors around eating.

If you don't have bribery or guilt to use with your kid, what's left? The best way to approach the dinner table is with Ellyn Satter's Division of Responsibility in mind. As the parent, you decide the what, when, and where of the meal, and your kid gets to decide how much and what they'll eat.

More specifically, you get to decide what food you'll serve at meals and snacks, along with when and where the food will be served. If the thought of nightly macaroni and cheese getting replaced with pasta primavera with shrimp, oysters, or duck confit has you reaching for your mixing spoons with sheer glee, remember your audience. I recommend having at least one to two foods available that you

KNOW your kids will eat. This doesn't mean you can't cook what you'd like; it just means having something like buttered noodles or bread and butter as a mainstay to ensure everyone gets *something* they like. It's also important to include all the major macronutrients at every meal: carbohydrates, protein, and fat. Bonus if the meal includes some fiber.

You get to decide what time the meal (and snacks) will be served and also where the meal will be served. I prefer to keep a fairly consistent routine around time and place, but you do what's best for your family. We typically have breakfast, morning snack, lunch, afternoon snack, and dinner (and an after-dinner snack often for our kids who have activities later in the evening). It's okay to offer food at these times and say that we won't be having food between these times.

It's important to remember that flexibility is key. If your kid isn't hungry for dinner and then wants cereal an hour later, let your kid have something so they don't go to bed hungry. While you likely don't want to make a habit of your child skipping dinner, ensuring they go to bed well-fed should take priority. The real rule to follow is that you want your kid to get enough to eat. Having enough to eat can be a real concern in many households and something to get support for from your medical and surrounding community, including food pantries and government-assisted programs. Food insecurity can lead to very abnormal eating patterns and subsequent disordered eating, so it's very important to get help and/or provide assistance to those with hunger needs.

Imagine you've whipped up your meal for the night and you can picture it on the table at 5:30 p.m.; now it's up to the child to decide what they want to eat and how much they want to eat. While this sounds easy, it can feel like a hard job at first. Refraining from any commentary about the food they eat outside of "Have you had enough to eat?" should be off limits. Comments that imply guilt and shame, like "Are you sure you want allllll that pasta?" or "That looks like wayyy too much butter" or "Haven't you had enough to eat already?" should also be left out of mealtime conversations.

Don't praise your kid either. Even a compliment like "Good for you for eating those veggies!" can put pressure on the kid to continue eating a particular food even if they don't like it, or it can make other kids at the table feel bad if they didn't choose to eat that particular food that day.

Trust yourself and your kid. Even if your kid goes through phases of eating only a limited group of foods or foods of a certain color or only energy-dense foods, they will eventually find their way. Trust your kid to honor their hunger and fullness. Your baby once knew when they'd had enough of the bottle or breast. It's a skill they're literally born with. Let them continue to hone that skill with your gentle guidance.

By acting as a gentle guide (channeling Mr. Rogers versus Oscar the Grouch), you'll teach your kid to trust themselves around one of our most basic human instincts and needs. Hunger, after all, is a biologically determined response similar to having to go to the bathroom. You'd never tell your kid that they've gone to the bathroom enough today or say, "Are you sure you really have to go?"

When it comes to the bathroom, there's no drama (toddlers excused). The body has needs that we don't question and honor. It's time to do the same honoring with your kid around food. Their body is wise and all-knowing, and now it's time for you to keep providing options (some research shows that a child needs to see a food 20 times before they'll consider eating it) and allow them a judgment-free zone to explore.

I promise that your dinner table will become so much more relaxed, and you'll actually be able to enjoy mealtime together. I love that our family time at the table can be spent making connections instead of being the food police who are constantly worried about what our kids are eating. I invite you to sit back and relax, and let your kid do the important work of discovering their likes and dislikes.

* * *

SUMMARY

Avoid praise that's positive or negative when it comes to what food your kid does (or doesn't) put on their plate. Never pressure or force your kid to eat a certain food or a certain amount of food. As parents, our job is to provide the food for the meal and decide what time we'll eat and where we'll eat. After that, we need to step back and trust that our kids will be able to listen to their own hunger and satiety cues so their needs are being met throughout the day or over the course of the week or month. Most importantly, maintain flexibility so that your kid gets enough to eat.

* * *

MANTRA

- I will choose what, when, and where my kids eat, and they will choose how much and what foods they'd like at any given snack or meal. I will trust my kids' bodies to let them know when they're satisfied both physically and emotionally.
- I will not praise any kid at the dinner table for choosing to try new foods or avoiding other foods.
- I will not bribe, force, cajole, shame, or blame my kid at the dinner table.

Sugar Isn't the Devil

I used to be *that* mom. The one who hovered near their kid at a birthday party to either refuse their slice of birthday cake or, at the very least, make sure their portion size was acceptable.

"No, thank you, we'll take the fruit instead."

I cringe now, thinking about the kind of messaging I was sending my kid. Something along the lines of "Hey, I know what's best for you and what you like, you can't do what your friends are doing, and the gathering at celebrations has nothing to do with food, joy, or pleasure."

Yikes. I meant well and was doing the best with the information I had, but in that moment, I was causing more harm than good. Yes, I was worried about sugar's effect on my kid's behavior and, if I'm being totally honest, what those "empty" calories would do to their body size, but I know now that both things simply aren't true. It never dawned on me that a kid's behavior after cake time could be, and very likely was, a measure that they were overstimulated. Have you been to a kid's birthday party? Every time we host a party, no matter how much fun I've had, I usually end up with a headache…the running, the jumping, the constant interactions, the noise, the different environ-ment, the friends all in one place, and being "on" for at least 90 minutes is both fun and exhausting.

If you see yourself in this birthday party scenario, you're not alone. Sugar has become the evil food of the day that moms every-where are wondering if they should eliminate or allow. When I was growing up, the worry was cholesterol from eggs and sugars in carbo-hydrates that spawned the SnackWell generation of eaters. Who knows what the diet industry will crown the next worst food you could eat for both your health and body size?

What matters is that you know your body relies on and needs carbohydrates, protein, and fats and fiber to work optimally. If you don't eat carbs, the body starts to shut down. Even the brain prefers carbohydrates as a fuel source. All that talk about brain fog? Maybe it's because *we aren't feeding our bodies enough carbohydrates* so much as the carbs we're putting into our bodies. Sugar also isn't a problem in a vacuum; it's important to understand how to balance your blood sugar, which can be done by weight neutral, additive measures versus dietary and restrictive approaches.

There's no denying that foods do affect your body in various ways. What if you feel like sugar has an adverse effect on you? You and only you can know how your body feels when you eat certain foods. If you feel fine after eating sugar at any time of the day, go for it! You absolutely have permission to eat sugar (or any other food) despite what diet culture dictates. You're a grown adult able to do what feels good and right for your body. And, no, sugar is NOT "addicting." (See more about my thoughts on that in the next section.) Remember, too, the very real "nocebo" effect in terms of food and your body. Simply believing a negative thought about how food will affect your body can actually produce a negative physical side effect.

What if you feel neutral toward sugar but notice a little headache or energy slump after eating sugar? The answer isn't necessarily to eliminate sugar altogether. The answer can be adding in more protein or fat-rich foods when eating high-sugar food items. A handful of nuts with your ice cream or some peanut butter with your chocolate or a glass of milk with your cookie can help stabilize blood sugar levels, which change within each individual based on the foods they consume and their body's unique ability to process sugar. Eating sugary foods with a meal can also be helpful as your body is likely taking in a combination of carbohydrates, protein, fat, and/or fiber with that meal. The combination of nutrients helps balance blood sugar and mitigate any potential adverse physical reactions. It's also important to know that you and your kid likely feel very differently after eating a certain amount of sugar. In general, kids are able to process and metabolize sugar much differently than adults. As we age, there is a change in the way we digest, absorb, and process nutrients. Think back to when you were a kid and you could eat handfuls of candy, and you never noticed anything outside of how yummy the candy tasted.

What if you're concerned about sugar's effect on your health? Christy Harrison, MPH, RD, author of the bestselling book *Anti-Diet, Reclaim Your Time, Money, Well-Being and Happiness Through Intuitive Eating*, teaches that "sugar is simply not the health scourge that diet culture makes it out to be, and in my view, there's no compelling reason to cut it out." Harrison goes on to say that the studies done on sugar's effects on the body are very mixed, to say the least. In fact, many of these studies show an association and not causation of sugar "causing" certain diseases, meaning there may be other things responsible for an individual's increased health risk. One of the things causing potential harm may be restrictive eating itself.

Harrison also reminds her readers that much of the nutrition research you hear about is NOT done via the gold-standard method, which includes a control group and is performed in a lab. Instead, research is done by asking people questions and relying on self-reporting to develop information. Even the amount of sugar people consume in these studies can be very misleading. Harrison highlighted a study that looked at the effects of sugar consumption on heart disease. The study divided participants into the lowest or highest quintile (or quartile) of sugar consumption. While you might think that the lowest consumption group ate little to no sugar a day, the study participants actually ate added sugar (equal to a sweetened food) at every meal or snack, PLUS dessert daily. The highest sugar consumption group ate the amount of sugar equivalent to seven full candy bars PER DAY. Looking at the information this way helps you understand that there's a lot more behind the scary headlines you read urging you to ban sugar (or any other food) from your diet.

Summary

Diet culture has demonized many foods over the course of time, and sugar happens to be the hot button food item for today. Making a certain food "bad" is diet culture's way of eliciting your shame and guilt response so you participate in the over $7-billion-a-year diet industry. People have enjoyed sugar for thousands of years, and there's nothing wrong with eating and enjoying sugar without guilt. If your body feels a little off after eating sugar, elimination isn't necessarily the answer. Eating it with meals or adding in protein with your sugary food or snack is a great way to help balance blood sugars, which differ in every individual. Lastly, kids and adults process sugar differently, so don't assume that your child has the same physical affects you do post-sugar consumption.

* * *

MANTRA

- I'm allowed to eat and enjoy any foods I want, including sugar.
- I can add protein-rich foods with my sugar consumption to help balance my blood sugar.
- It's okay to desire sugar and enjoy sugar's pleasurable taste and experience.
- I'm in charge of my body and knowing what tastes and feels good.

The Truth About Food Addiction

"Ugh, someone get this bag of chips away from me!"

"I have no idea how I got to the end of this Girl Scout cookie sleeve!"

"I can't even keep ice cream in my house anymore because it literally talks to me through the freezer door, and it's just too tempting!"

"I can't trust myself around any chocolate bar. Period."

"That stuff is so addicting!!!!"

Do any of these comments sound familiar? For a long time, I felt like I couldn't have any "forbidden" foods in my kitchen because I was sure I was addicted. What did you believe was your food "addiction?" Was it brownies? Cookies? Salty foods? Bagels?

It wasn't just the food itself; it was the way you tore into your food de jour with a sense of animalism and inability to stop. Like you had to put soap on the rest of your cake or pan of brownies and put them into the garbage in order to stop, and even then, you opened the garbage once, if not twice, checking to see if there was a corner or piece that might still be edible.

Have you ever felt like you just can't stop eating because you're actually physically addicted to food? Like the genetic gods messed up your DNA and you literally have an addiction gene that's constantly misfiring?

It's time to set the record straight about food addiction. Spoiler alert: There is NO such thing as food addiction. Period. Let's start out with a definition of addiction.

Addiction is defined as the fact or condition of being addicted to a particular substance, thing, or activity. In terms of substances, addiction is a neuropsychological disorder characterized by a persistent urge to use a drug, despite substantial harm and other negative consequences.

With a physiological addiction to something, there's the classic tolerance and withdrawal piece as well. Tolerance meaning you need more and more of the substance to elicit the same response, and withdrawal meaning you need more of the substance just to avoid adverse reactions like nausea, vomiting, cold sweats, chills, anxiety, and depression. For those addicted to drugs, the only thing that makes withdrawal go away is more of that drug.

The tolerance and withdrawal hallmarks of addiction don't hold true with food, even sugar. If we have a sugar crash, eating whole foods and protein helps us feel better; more sugar will not necessarily help us feel better. In fact, we often feel sick if we eat too much sugar before we feel physically full.

I don't know about you, but one bite of sugar is pleasurable; I don't need 50 bites in order to sense that pleasure. One bite of a freshly baked chocolate chip cookie or pumpkin bread and I'm fully aware of the pleasure. We don't need more food to elicit a pleasurable response. If we're truly paying attention to being in the moment while we eat, we'll notice at a certain point near satiation that our food actually doesn't taste as good. Chemical changes occur in our taste receptors to signal to our body that we've had enough to eat. Also, the same dopamine centers in our brain that "light up" from drugs and food are also stimulated by hugs, music, sex, snuggling your baby, falling in love, and being recognized for an achievement.

When people talk about food addiction, very often the proposed solution is abstinence. Feeling crazy around sugar? Don't eat it again...EVER. The problem is the abstinence model of food for the purpose of controlling weight or for complete food group elimination is largely ineffective. At some point in time, you'll want some sugar or carbs or whatever "evil" you've sworn off. Trust me; it's a natural human desire that can't be ignored or denied for the rest of your life.

Abstinence is usually suggested as a way to feel less "out of control around food," yet the irony is that the out-of-control feeling usually stems from trying to control yourself through restriction. As a reminder, restriction is what leads to what I refer to as reactionary (aka binge) eating and more feelings of being out of control with food. Your body's natural reaction to restriction is to eat more food. You can call it a binge if you want, but that word often has such a negative connotation and doesn't accurately describe what's happening in your body, which is a normal and natural reaction to deprivation.

If you label yourself an addict, you might logically conclude the treatment is to abstain. To translate this to food doesn't work, even though you may feel "out of control" with food. As we've talked about, abstaining from food (or multiple food groups) is correlated with making things worse in the long run. It's no surprise that your body turns to high-carbohydrate and energy-dense food after deprivation. It's wired to seek calories that are quick and easy to digest when you don't consume sufficient energy. To feel calm and in control of your food, you must stop restricting.

What happens when you turn to food as a coping strategy when you feel emotional discomfort? Does that mean you're addicted to food? In short, the answer is no. Turning to food as a source of comfort and pleasure is not only normal but a natural human experience. Using food as a way to cope is pretty innocuous in comparison to the many other more harmful coping mechanisms at your disposal. Here's where our culture gets it wrong with regard to food. Instead of teaching to reduce shame and stigma with our behaviors around food, you're told to increase your rigidity and rules around food, which only leads to a preoccupation and feeling "addicted" to certain foods. The perfect catch-22.

The truth is that food is intended to be enjoyed and pleasurable. We want our pleasure centers to light up so that we are motivated to seek out food for continued nourishment and survival. Yes, remember we need to eat to SURVIVE!

Allow yourself to take a big deep breath, knowing that you can't be addicted to food, and there's nothing wrong with you if you're drawn to a particular food repeatedly. If you notice feeling "obsessed" around certain foods, you're very likely restricting your food intake either physically (actual food intake) or mentally (what you tell yourself has an effect on the amount of food you eat). There's nothing wrong with you, you weren't born with a problem, and you don't need more willpower.

After learning this, you might be wondering: I still want to know if it's okay to avoid any foods that I think are "bad?"

You may be a religious label reader or fastidious box or bag checker before tossing an item into your cart, and letting go of this might feel hard. You read about things like partially hydrogenated oils or food dyes or gluten and want to know if it's really okay to eat these so-called "addictive" foods.

The short answer is yes, you can choose to eat or avoid certain foods, but there's a big caveat.

If you choose to avoid a certain food, you must be sure that you're getting enough macronutrients and that your choice to avoid certain food ingredients must not have a negative effect on your life. The reason to avoid these foods should come from a completely weight-neutral place, too. We have to be very careful about the emergence of orthorexic tendencies (a condition that includes symptoms of obsessive behavior in pursuit of a healthy diet) in this arena of "cutting out." Of course, there's an exception for people who have a medical allergy to gluten, like those with celiac disease, which I'll discuss later in more detail.

* * *

SUMMARY

Food addiction is a term that has largely been popularized by individuals looking to gain from this scare tactic. Addiction is really a misnomer when it comes to food. You don't need more food to feel its effects, and you also don't need more food in order to avoid feeling bad. With food, both of these traditional addiction characteristics are false. If you notice yourself feeling obsessed with or eating more food than you normally would in a sitting, the best thing to do is find out where you might be restricting your food intake throughout the day. By getting your energy needs met and giving yourself full allowance to eat what and how much you want throughout the day, there's very often a dramatic reduction in binge or reactionary eating and your thoughts about food. Who knew that more food would actually be the answer to feeling relaxed around food?

* * *

MANTRA

- There's no such thing as food addiction.
- If I'm feeling crazy around food, where might I be restricting my food intake during the day?
- There's no right or wrong way to enjoy food.

Halloween Candy and Other Holidays

As a child, I used to love Halloween. The costumes! The candy! The group of friends running house to house shouting, "Trick or treat!" My mom was the queen of coming up with the last-minute costume that was dressy enough to pass as a costume but not too much fuss. Enter the cowgirl, cheerleader, and hobo with the stick slung over my shoulder with pillowcase attached. The best part of Halloween was sorting my candy into categories. I can still see the piles and piles spread on the kitchen floor perfectly sorted, with some of the best (hello, Snickers) candy getting sampled throughout my precious sort. I was always a saver, keeping those Reese's, Red Vines, and Snickers bars for those dark days of January when my sister's candy was long gone and I could torment her with my stash.

Luckily my days of feeling anxious around food came well past my days of going door to door, and my hope is that our kids can continue to enjoy this holiday as I did—without stress or worry about sugar consumption or body size. There's a lot of noise these days about the dangers of sugar, so even the most well-intentioned parents can get it wrong when it comes to handling unlimited Snickers bars (best when frozen!).

Do you watch your kids tearing through their Halloween stash, peeling candy after candy and feel a little anxious or like you're a bad mom for letting your kids eat all of that stuff? Isn't everybody sugar-free and gluten-free these days?

Do you have the "candy fairy" take away your kid's candy and leave behind a toy?

Do you let your kids eat what they want on Halloween and donate the rest the next morning in an attempt to just "get it out of the house?"

While these options might feel tempting, none of these tactics will help promote a relationship of trust between your child and their food. If you take candy away from your child, that shows them that not only do YOU not trust them, but THEY also can't trust themselves around food. When you restrict your kid's intake, you'll very likely find them sneaking and hoarding food down the road. Anytime there's secrecy around food, you and your kid will likely feel shame and guilt, which are two of the feelings you want to avoid in terms of food since both tend to trigger interfering with your uninhibited and natural food consumption. As a reminder, you don't want to teach your kids that certain foods are good and others are bad. Demonizing food only makes a healthy relationship with food more difficult. The goal is to treat food neutrally. Yes, the KitKat and the carrot are both just food, and being able to choose both at various times for various reasons is totally acceptable.

Most often, it's the adults that need to deal with their own anxieties around food so their kids can enjoy the holiday. Think back to your trick or treating days. What was it like for you? Did your parents take away your candy? Did they seem anxious around food? If you can relax and let your children self-regulate, they will very likely lose that first night of trick or treat excitement over time and/or have an internal sense of how much is enough.

Whether it's candy, ice cream, carrots, apples, or potato chips, overconsumption of any particular food will lead anyone to lose their appeal toward that food. I think back to my waitressing days at The Olive Garden and remember how I couldn't touch a breadstick or bowl of minestrone soup for months after working there. Remember in college when you swore you couldn't touch one more bowl of ramen noodles even if someone paid you?

You still might be dreading Halloween because you're thinking, *Well, I can't trust my kids to self-regulate, they'll never stop, and there's no way I can get all food to be neutral in my mind. So what should I do? I still feel like there are too many temptations, there's too much sugar, and I have too many worries about being "bad" around my food choices.*

You might even be tempted to say these common things to your kids:

"Keep that stuff away from me."

"Tonight we'll be bad, but tomorrow we'll eat healthy."

"We're being so naughty right now."

All of these thoughts come because of diet culture. Here's what you need to know. Eating any kind of food is never bad. All foods can be enjoyed without feeling guilty. Contrary to popular belief, sugar isn't the devil and won't kill you. And when you allow yourself to have what you want and stop restricting, food will magically lose its "power" over you and you'll naturally find a stopping point that feels right for your body.

Here are my top-10 ghoulish goals for Halloween (or any holiday with lots of goodies):

1. Give your kids (and yourself) regular meals and snacks throughout the day. No skipping meals or food groups to

"save up" your allotment to be spent later on candy. Restricting your intake during the day will only make you more likely to binge on high-sugar, high-carbohydrate foods later in the day.

2. Get in on the fun with your kids. Dress up, tell spooky stories, play a fun game, carve a pumpkin, and play some favorite songs like "Monster Mash."

3. When your kids get their candy, allow them to sort, organize, and ohh and ahh at their treasures. LET THEM EAT WHATEVER THEY WANT. You can remind them to check in with their bodies and if they eat too much, their tummy might hurt, but you'll trust them to know when they want to stop.

4. Repeat this for the next day. Let them eat whatever they want, whenever they want. Of course, continue to serve regular meals and snacks throughout the day.

5. On the second day and for the rest of the week, you can store the candy out of sight but not hidden. Allow your kids to pick a piece of candy to have along with meals or snacks (we start this at lunchtime). I do not recommend having a candy fairy come or having the candy just disappear overnight. If you ask kids if there are any pieces they want to donate, and they do want to give up some of their non-favorite pieces (looking at you, Tootsie Rolls and Smarties), that's okay because it's their decision and not yours. Remember that you want to give the message that you trust your kids and they can trust themselves around food.

6. The following week, go back to offering the candy with/after dinner and not during lunch or snack time.

7. Talk with your kids about what Halloween was like for you. Tell your kids what your favorite candy is, and ask

them about their favorite candy! Make this holiday a time for you to connect and learn more about one another.

8. Don't talk about calories or make judgments about yourself or your kids based on what they eat, and don't ask kids if they're sure they really want something. As long as you've given the green light to enjoy an item for dessert, you let them decide what they want without adding in any shame or guilt.

9. It's a personal choice if you want to leave out sticky foods if your child has particular candies that don't work with braces.

10. While I follow Ellyn Satter's Division of Responsibility by letting kids decide what to eat and how much, I think it's okay to give a "how much" rule around candy and dessert. After you've given your kid full access for a couple of days, you can absolutely say that one portion or serving is enough for today and that you can look forward to another serving tomorrow. You can decide what that amount is based on your child's age (a 2-year-old will likely have a different amount than a 12-year-old).

You can ignore all the suggestions about how to offer candy and simply watch your kid's natural response and process. Despite an initial period where kids might go a little overboard (this is especially true if there's any restriction), most kids will lose interest over time. This process of consuming less over time is backed by science and is called habituation. Kids really can be trusted with food.

* * *

SUMMARY

It's so important to be a great role model for your kids during the holidays so they can grow up in an environment that celebrates love, joy, and connection, as opposed to emphasizing anxiety around food and their body. Let kids enjoy their candy, and use the steps above to have a framework for how to enjoy their candy over time. You want to teach your kids that you trust them and they can trust themselves around food. Skipping meals to "save up" for later usually ends with a binge, so be sure to stay well-fed throughout the day. Recognize that you, just like your child, will likely eat more during the holidays, and that's totally normal. Your body is such a sophisticated system that it will automatically compensate for the additional foods you eat by craving a little less food the following day, days, or weeks. This is true for any holiday: Thanksgiving turkey, Christmas cookies, or Valentine's chocolates all apply. It all evens out in the end, and your body already has a sophisticated built-in system to figure out the details.

MANTRA

- Holidays are meant to be enjoyed, and food is part of that enjoyment.
- I'm allowed to eat what I want without feeling shame or guilt.
- I can relax around food so I can enjoy connecting with my friends and family.

Stop Commenting on What/How Much Your Kid Eats

My nana used to constantly be worried about how much food everyone had eaten at our weekly Sunday night dinners. As the matriarch of our Italian family, her job was to make sure each one of us had enough pasta with sugo (sauce). As soon as Uncle Tony's plate was empty, she'd be coaxing him into round two! If my plate didn't have enough food, she'd say, "That's not enough, honey; why don't you go get some more food to eat or you're going to be too hungry!"

This was her way of showing love. Noticing if there was too little and encouraging more was her way of making sure that we were cared for in the most basic way. Does this sound familiar in your house? How many times have you praised your child for eating their whole plate? Or maybe chided them for having seconds? Or asked if they were sure they were still hungry or really "needed" a particular food or serving? While these all seem like totally normal parenting responses, I'm going to encourage you to let go of any praise around what your child eats or scolding them for eating what you might consider "too much."

This is especially important if you have more than one child.

Parents can all agree that every child has different likes and dislikes, and every child has a built-in system that tells them how much food they need to run optimally. Praising or shaming a child for the amount of food they eat can cause tremendous difficulty for that child to be able to listen to and honor their unique internal hunger and satiation cues. Reading Virginia Sole-Smith's book, *The Eating Instinct: Food Culture, Body Image, and Guilt in America,* opened my eyes to a wide variety of ways that kids in the same family eat because of medical or other conditions.

As a parent, it's natural to want to control many things about your child, especially their food intake. I want to assure you that your child's weight isn't something you need to add to your "control this" or "monitor this" or "fix this" list. Everybody has their own largely genetically controlled weight set point (the weight that your body naturally defends both in absence and excess of food) and has to work very hard to go above or below that set point. People of all shapes and sizes have always existed and will continue to exist, regardless of any attempts at control.

What would it be like in your house if you were able to let go of monitoring your child's intake? What if the only question you asked your child was, "Have you had enough to eat?" Of course, if you're concerned your child isn't eating enough, it's time to reach out to your pediatrician or a HAES-aligned dietitian.

* * *

SUMMARY

While it's up to you to offer what and when your child will eat during the day, remember that they get to choose HOW MUCH to eat. Their body knows best, and it's counterproductive to make commentary around how much food they should be eating. Most food photos in magazines show diet portions and not real-life portion sizes. There's no need to count calories for your child. Let your child choose the amount of food they need, and you can remind yourself to simply ask your child, "Have you had enough to eat?" Avoid praising one child's eating habits over another at or away from the dinner table. Even praising a child for being adventurous can be hard for another child who doesn't like a large variety of foods. Trying to get positive praise around any kind of food behavior isn't the message we want to send as it encourages a child to be performative rather than eat intuitively or from their own sense of body autonomy.

Mantra

- My child knows their body best.
- It's not my job to dictate my child's food intake.
- I don't need to second guess the amount of food my child is eating.

Recognize Restriction (Cutting Out Foods Unless Medically Necessary)

We were surrounded by $11-a-pop green juice drinkers, SoulCycle devotees, and devout "health" food fanatics when we lived in San Francisco. The Golden Arches were nowhere in sight, and eating at restaurants with multiple menus to accommodate special diets was the norm. A preschool snack, a birthday party cake, or a playdate offering very often had to be gluten-free, nut-free, and sugar-free. I don't think there was ever a time that we weren't accommodating a particular "allergy" or food "sensitivity" at any school or social event we attended.

This California trend seems to be mainstream these days as there's so much information bombarding us about elimination diets, primarily the elimination of flour, gluten, sugar, and dairy. The truth is that at the root of these restrictions very often lies the fear that these foods will make us or our kids "unhealthy" or "fat" or negatively affect behavior or our ability to achieve peak physical performance. For most people who eliminate foods, there's no scientific or medical reason for elimination. Self- or parent-diagnosis is incredibly common and can be really dangerous.

From a medical standpoint, even dietitians specializing in GI issues will be the first to tell you that an elimination diet isn't meant to be followed forever. It is a tool used to tease out what's really going on in the body and educate you about how your body feels when you eat certain things. They aren't intended as the religion or platform for failure or success that they've become.

You might be wondering why I have air quotes around the words "allergy" and "sensitivity." Did you know that less than 1% of the population actually has celiac disease and another less than 1% of the population has a wheat allergy? As a reminder, gluten is a protein naturally found in grains like wheat, rye, and barley. Both of these conditions are improved with the elimination of gluten for celiac and wheat for the wheat allergy. If you don't have one of these diagnosed conditions, there really isn't a good reason to eliminate this food group. Period. There's no scientific evidence that gluten causes inflammation, brain fog, or bloating. Pause and let that really sink in.

Lately, alternative practitioners, in particular, have found high interest in gluten-free as a cure-all. Unfortunately, there's no good evidence that eating gluten-free cures ailments, and eliminating gluten from your diet can actually cause harm. "Healing the gut" with gluten-free can actually mask disordered eating.

The more foods you remove from your diet, the less your digestive system is able to digest and easily absorb. The coating of the intestines actually becomes less diverse. This is why it's so important to address underlying disordered eating versus eliminating foods for GI issues. You may actually need to replace and not restrict your gluten intake. If you're concerned that you do have a food allergy that's causing GI distress, it's best to see a medically trained allergist and rely on testing available through your doctor. Avoid any at-home testing kits or procedures or alternative practitioners that claim to know your body's sensitivities through hair analysis and other measures that aren't scientifically based. Some research has also shown gentle movement like yoga and meditation to be helpful for GI distress.

Many disordered eaters decide to give up a food group for what they claim are health reasons, but the real reason is the promise of weight loss or perfect health. They also end up restricting, which inevitably leads to reactionary or binge eating behaviors. If you want to safely remove gluten, you must replace the gluten in your diet with other non-gluten carbs and starches. Failing to add additional foods in to replace the foods that have been taken away is critical.

Make sure you ask yourself, by avoiding this ingredient, will you have to skip dinners out with your family? Will you have to skip parties? Will you have to spend hours shopping for and cooking your food? Will you have to starve yourself if there are no other options? Will this negatively impact your life? If the answer is yes, then I would not recommend skipping this ingredient or food group.

If I still haven't convinced you to go buy a fresh baguette, consider that there also aren't studies showing lasting weight loss for those adhering to gluten-free diets. I can hear you through the pages telling me that you know you don't have an actual allergy but you do indeed have a sensitivity to gluten. There is something called non-specified gluten sensitivity. Studies have been done on groups of gluten-sensitive individuals where they've been given wheat in a double-blind scenario (participants and researchers don't know what foods actually had gluten in them), and the result is that even these groups have something else other than a reaction to the actual food going on because gluten didn't consistently produce an adverse reaction in this group.

So how can this be? What can explain the very real and adverse reactions you may be experiencing? Enter the nocebo effect again. If you're told something is good for you, you believe it and have a positive reaction. If you're told something is bad for you, you believe it and have a negative reaction. This seems crazy, but it's well documented. The mind-body connection is incredibly strong. Remember our parents taking us out for Chinese food and saying, "No MSG, please," to the wait staff? Well, it turns out, there was no significant reaction to MSG, and the whole thing was based on a single doctor's anecdotal experience, not scientific studies, yet many people were convinced MSG was a problem.

What about cutting out other foods if you're vegan or have religious beliefs around food? I would encourage ethical vegans (those who choose not to eat an animal or animal byproduct for ethical reasons) or those who eat kosher, for example, to make sure they examine their reasons behind their way of eating. If the choice is truly weight neutral or meant to create a deeper connection with a higher power, then this way of eating will likely work as long as there's plenty of food and nutrients available outside of the eliminated foods.

What if you choose to eat vegetarian or vegan and struggle with wanting to eat meat or cheese periodically? Being flexible with food choices doesn't mean you're a bad person or that you can't make room for some foods some of the time. Your choices and priorities will change on a daily basis, which is why it's so important to stay in touch with your body's natural wants and desires around food. You can eat one way a majority of the time and still leave room for optionality based on your desires. Remember, there are plenty of vegetarians who like to eat bacon and affectionately refer to themselves as flexitarians. No gymnastics splits required to be a flexitarian, simply flexibility with your food choices on any given day.

Several religious groups observe fasting around various holidays. If you're really struggling with moving past restrictions and feel that fasting for prolonged periods could be triggering for you, I highly recommend that you speak with your church or synagogue's leader to discuss your individual situation. I'd be really surprised if they weren't empathetic to and willing to work with you regarding your situation.

One other thing I hear clients asking me about is fasting for medical appointments. Unfortunately, this can't be avoided. This is absolutely fuel for the intermittent fasting crowd's fire to say that we have to fast for appointments and survive, so why not do it all the time? The point is that our bodies are not built for prolonged or repeated fasting. Yes, you and I can handle the one-off times we need to avoid food prior to a medical procedure, blood draw or test, but we need consistent and regular food/meals the majority of time. Just because you can do something short-term doesn't mean you should do something long-term. What's more is there's absolutely no science to back these claims. The best thing to do is to make your appointment as close to first thing in the morning as possible and enjoy food as soon as you're able to after your appointment.

It's important to remember that health is experienced on a spectrum. Health isn't black or white; health happens in the gray zone. When you're coming from a place of neutrality, you can experiment and often find that foods you once thought were off-limits actually don't bother you anymore, or you feel comfortable experimenting with different amounts of food and in different combinations. Simply using the word "choose" around food choices instead of "can't" can be incredibly powerful. "I choose to have this," or "I don't choose to have this," is much more empowering than "I can't have this or that." No foods are forbidden.

Sometimes we make a personal decision to eat a food (that is deemed "unhealthy") that is worth more than the potential adverse real or perceived health effects. This doesn't make you a bad person. You can choose foods based on your physical health, and you can choose foods based on your mental health, both of which are equally important parts of the health equation. And remember, no single snack, meal, day, or month of eating a certain way will "ruin" your health.

One final note: Please use caution when it comes to alternative medicine testing for food sensitivities. There really is no validity to applied kinesiology (aka muscle testing), cell testing, hair testing, or IGG testing. These tests usually result in some kind of minor or major food or food group elimination which can be very dangerous. My mentor, Isabel Foxen Duke, taught me that there are so many ways to improve health (including food-related conditions like diabetes) that have *nothing* to do with restriction. For instance, moving your body, getting enough fiber/protein, eating regular meals, etc., are all things you can ADD to your life to help manage blood sugar without actively restricting anything.

In summary, if you're considering making changes to your diet, please consider the following:

1. This is the most important, so listen up! Ask yourself, what is the motivation behind making this change? If—deep down—the answer has anything to do with changing or altering your body shape or weight, this means it's based on diet culture and not at all in your best interest. If the motivation is completely weight-neutral (aka I don't care what happens to my shape or weight), and focused on actual health (balancing blood sugars, improving digestion), then carry on.

2. Am I approaching health as something I can fail or achieve? If the answer is yes, you're inevitably going to fail. Why? Because nobody is perfect when it comes to food, nor do we want to strive for perfection because there is no such thing. Health happens on a spectrum. Think of a blue color spectrum that spans from light to dark. The color is always blue regardless of where you point on the spectrum. Just like a color spectrum, our health is constantly changing, shifting, and fluctuating. Learning to

live in the gray, not black or white, is key to long-term recovery.

3. Ask yourself, is this new change or behavior increasing or decreasing my stress level? The whole point of making change is to improve your overall health or wellness. If you take action and it adds to your mental or physical stress, it's not worth doing. Change needs to be both sustainable and evoke feelings of sanity versus stress. Any pursuit of health should leave us feeling better mentally. It should not leave us feeling obsessed or inadequate. If we don't follow our new "rule," will it leave us feeling like we failed, or can we look at the inevitable deviation from what we intended as no big deal? There's not a wagon to fall off of, and our food choices are not the number one determinant of our health.

4. If I have a true allergy or sensitivity, then it's crucial to replace any potential lost macronutrients as a result of restriction. For example, if you have a gluten sensitivity, make sure you're eating potatoes, rice, or other gluten-free products to make up for lost carbohydrates! This is often referred to as unintentional restriction, but it can be just as dangerous as an intentional restriction.

* * *

SUMMARY

Cutting out foods when there's no diagnosed medical condition can have adverse physical and mental effects on your body. Really examining the reason why you're eliminating foods and taking an honest look at your beliefs about certain foods can open the door to food allowance and being able to relax around foods. Instead of looking to cut things out, where can you add foods that could be helpful? Where can you experiment with foods and allow the body to heal with the addition versus subtraction of foods (especially disordered eaters with known GI distress)? If you're dealing with GI distress, consider adding foods back into your diet instead of eliminating more foods. Some studies have shown meditation or gentle movement, like yoga, can also be helpful in healing GI distress.

* * *

MANTRA

- Instead of cutting things out, what foods can I add in?
- Am I really and truly needing to avoid this food because of a diagnosed medical condition, or could I be avoiding it out of fear?
- Restriction in any amount will result in reactionary eating. I can enjoy my food without guilt.

Section 5

Navigating a Diet-Obsessed World

Talking with Your Kid's Doctor

I sat on the too-high exam table with feet dangling while I tried to wrangle my wiggly baby on my lap. We had barely survived the trauma of her height and weight check and now had to wait again. After what felt like an hour, the doctor arrived for an exam, and my child latched on to me as if we had imaginary Velcro connectors.

It didn't take long for the doctor to comment on my child's height and weight. She turned the computer screen towards me so I could see the plot points on the graph and started asking questions that felt accusatory and uncomfortable.

Does your child get enough exercise?

Is your child eating fruits and vegetables?

Are you concerned about their eating habits?

At this point, I was sweating with my cling-on toddler pressed against me. I kept glancing back at the poster wall to see if maybe there was an escape window I missed, as I felt like I'd been teleported into a courtroom. I swear, your honor, I didn't do anything wrong.

Maybe you've been in this very situation yourself. Maybe your doctor has asked you uncomfortable questions that lead you to question your parenting (especially around food) or what you do with your own choices around food and movement.

I first want to empathize with you and remind you that parenting is hard work, and if it feels hard, you've done nothing wrong. You're right where you're meant to be. Every child comes into this world with a unique blueprint for their body size and shape, which is largely determined by genetics. The amount of food your kid needs to maintain the body size that helps them function optimally is also predetermined, which is why helping your kid learn to listen to their body and their own intuition around food is so important.

While I truly believe that no doctor means harm, (after all, that is the oath they take to become a doctor), doctors are some of the most fatphobic people in our society. I've heard some horror stories about the way both kids and parents are treated. Blame it on a lack of nutrition information taught in medical school, societal misinformation about the effects of food and movement on body size, and the complicated interconnectedness of big pharma, weight loss, and physicians who stand to gain from surgical procedures to "fix" body sizes. There's no way a simplified chart can give the whole story of your child's health.

None of this is a fix for the judgment you feel when you or your kid are being weight-shamed at your doctor's office. A study highlighted by Christy Harrison shows that many of the adverse health conditions that have traditionally been linked with higher weight are actually very highly correlated with the amount of weight stigma an individual has experienced throughout their life, along with the negative effects of weight cycling. So, what's a mama to do?

I highly recommend that you connect with your doctor outside of your appointment to lay some ground rules about how you'd like the topic of food and weight to go during regular checkups. The first thing you can request is a blind weight, meaning your kid doesn't see the number on the scale. You can also request the same for yourself or even request no weight at all. Asking why weight is needed as an adult can be helpful, so you know if the weight measure is necessary. There's a lot of controversy over weight being a necessary data point, but you absolutely can opt out if hearing a number is problematic for you.

Additionally, you can request that your doctor doesn't talk about your kid's weight in front of them. You can assure your doctor that you'd be happy to talk on the phone at any time should there be any concerns. As an added bit of information, I would be most concerned about any weight loss over time versus any weight gain. Remember that kids are supposed to be growing and gaining weight, especially as they enter puberty. On average, kids during this time period of growth will gain about 40 pounds in 4 years from age 10 to 14 in girls and a little later for boys. According to Katherine Zavodni, MPH, RDN, weight gain in kids is normal and necessary.

Because you very likely want to partner with your child's provider, I highly recommend a team approach versus me against you. Using words like "we" and "together" helps diffuse any need for there to be somebody who's right and somebody who's wrong.

This script from Dr. Katja Rowell's letter to physicians is one that I think is very effective if you have a larger-bodied child.

Dear healthcare provider,
I am aware that my child's BMI places them in the "over-
weight/obese" range. Please do not discuss my child's growth chart,
weight, or BMI in front of my child.
If you have concerns about my child's growth, please talk with me
when my child is not present.
This request is in line with the 2016 American Academy of Pediatrics
statement that providers should not talk about weight with children

and adolescents. This is based on research focusing on weight causes harm, including:

Discussion about growth charts and weight can frighten and confuse children.

Focusing on weight leads to restrictive feeding, which interferes with hunger and fullness cues and leads to overeating.

Focusing on weight leads to dieting, which is associated with increased weight, depression, and eating disorders over time.

I am happy to talk with you about my child's health habits, variety of food, sleep, screen time, activity, and emotional wellbeing. We follow the evidence-supported Responsive Feeding model 4, grounded in Satter's Division of Responsibility of Feeding, which the AAP, CDC, WIC, and WHO recommend as best practice.

Sincerely,

Your Patient's Parent

Dietitians Anna Lutz, MPH, RD, LDN, CEDRD-S, and Elizabeth Davenport, MPH, RD, LD, who formed Sunny Side up Nutrition, also give these tips to further personalize this letter:

We have had clinicians make assumptions about my child's eating habits based on weight. We can assure you my child does not regularly drink soda or juice, enjoys movement, and is provided with a variety of foods. As a family, we eat meals together and limit screen time.

A focus on weight is particularly problematic in our family. There is a strong family history of eating disorders, which are known to have a genetic component and are among the deadliest of all mental illnesses.

A helpful script for foster care:

My child has a history of being in foster care, and we suspect they experienced food insecurity. Dieting and restrictive feeding create food insecurity for a child. A focus on weight and restrictive feeding will be a continuation of my child feeling like they will not get enough food. This will make things worse. Instead, we are using a Responsive Feeding approach to help my child heal from their previous experience.

If you have a suspected concern:

We do have concerns about our child's eating behaviors and are seeking out professional help from a psychotherapist/registered dietitian to support our child and us. However, we feel strongly that a focus on weight will only cause harm.

While you might not feel comfortable with all of the suggestions listed here, hopefully, these ideas will give you the support you need to ensure a safe environment for your child at their doctor's visits.

* * *

Summary

It's important for your child to hear weight-positive messaging both at home and at the doctor's office. Weight stigma is real and has material, detrimental effects on health over time. Children don't need to hear confusing or punishing messages about food or their body, and you have a right to ask that any weight discussions be done with you in private, and that weight either be measured with your kid's back to the scale or not at all unless there's a medical necessity. Using a pre-written letter like the one provided by Dr. Rowell can be extremely helpful if your child has a larger body.

Mantra

- My kid isn't wrong because of their size; I have not ruined my child.
- I can find many weight-neutral ways to improve my child's health.
- I can provide consistent meals and snacks for my kid and encourage movement without tying either of those to a particular weight outcome.

When Your Kid Is Vegan/Vegetarian

I'll be the first to admit that meat is NOT my jam. A little bit of chicken from time to time and some fish, but the rest is a hard NO. Does this mean that I have disordered eating? No it doesn't, but it might be a sign of trouble. Let me explain.

If your child or teenager suddenly declares they're becoming a vegetarian, it's time to get curious and ask some questions. This may not be a sign of potential trouble or it could be a sign of disordered eating. The first and most important thing to do is talk with your kid about why they're suddenly interested in this change. People choose to be vegetarian for religious reasons, animal rights reasons, "health" reasons, environmental reasons, or sometimes because of food texture preference. Some may inadvertently become vegetarian because of their food access situation. You can ask your kid, "Are you worried about your health, the planet, or your weight?" Once you understand where they're coming from, you can find ways to support them.

While not all vegetarians have an eating disorder, people with eating disorders often report having been a vegan or vegetarian. By assigning a culturally accepted label to disordered eating, individuals who fear eating fat can slip under the radar. If you think your kid is choosing this new way of eating because of a fear of fat or weight gain, it's a good idea to talk with your doctor or find a weight-neutral dietitian. You may want to pay particular attention to this new way of eating if this behavior is coupled with wearing large or baggy clothing.

You may want to encourage your kids who want to eat less meat or dairy products to have a more flexitarian approach. Merriam-Webster defines a flexitarian as "one whose normally meatless diet occasionally includes meat or fish." If your kid is worried about the planet or animal rights, talk with them about the benefits of buying meat from a local farm or at your local farmer's market. Call a local farmer and find out how you can help the environment in your own community. Find companies that are committed to both saving the planet and allowing their animals to live a happy and humane life. Sometimes just finding out how your kid can play an active role in the process can allow them to have some comfort around eating certain foods. And remember, there are many non-food ways to save the planet, too.

Let your kid know they don't have to use black or white thinking. It doesn't have to be all or nothing. It can be AND sometimes. I like to eat tofu AND sometimes a piece of bacon. I like to eat vegetables and grains most of the time AND sometimes meat. This flexibility can help your child navigate issues in their life that they'll encounter off their plate, too. The AND sometimes approach is a great philosophy to adopt in life as well.

You may want to explore if any of your kid's friends are making this change, too. Are their teachers or coaches talking about this? Have they read anything on social media? Are they feeling pressured to save the planet with what they put on their fork? Regardless of what your kid chooses, don't attach any moral righteousness to any way of eating. There's no right or wrong, good or bad, better or worse way to eat. Children and teens can easily get wrapped up in black or white thinking. Show them that there's a wide variety of ways to eat and all options are valid.

The most important thing is to ensure that a growing child/teenager is getting enough food to eat. Always offer something you know your kids can eat, but don't feel pressured to make a separate meal. We have various meat preferences at our house, and I often leave the protein as an add-in for rice, pasta, or salads. I highly recommend talking with a HAES dietitian as a great way to make sure a variety of nutrients and energy intake are being met if your kid insists on a strict vegan/vegetarian diet.

* * *

SUMMARY

If your child suddenly wants to become a vegetarian or vegan, take some time to ask them why they want to make this change. Once you understand their reasoning, you can help support them in being flexible when possible, finding other ways to support environmental/animal rights, or working with a dietitian who can devise a plan that will ensure your growing child/teenager is getting enough food for optimal physical and mental growth.

* * *

MANTRA

- There's room for flexible eating and no need to stick with a rigid protocol.
- I can choose to focus on a variety of foods.

- There's no moral virtue in eating a certain way. All ways of eating are acceptable.
- No single individual can eradicate the environmental crisis by what they choose to eat. There are many ways outside of food to help the environment.

Spotting Red Flags and Getting Help Quickly

We sat at the base of the mountain with the sun warming our faces after a final morning of cutting through thick white powder.

My usually very chatty daughter sat quietly.

"Everything okay, honey?" I asked.

"Yeah, Mom, I'm just tired," she said quietly.

One flag up.

I finally got lunch to the table, which is no small feat when you're clunking around in ski boots, balancing a tray of steaming soup and sandwiches.

My daughter picked at her lunch, which was odd as she normally has a good appetite, especially after a morning of skiing.

"Are you sure you're okay?" I prodded.

"Yesssss, Mooooooom," she pleaded.

Another flag up.

We gobbled down our food, and clomped back to our hotel to grab our bags and hit the road. About 30 minutes into our drive, my daughter got sick in the car. Our deepest sympathies to the garbage person who found our car seat next to their dumpster in the Lake Tahoe area.

I knew there were warning signs, but I let them go. In this case, it was altitude sickness, and my daughter was feeling better by the time we got back to the city, which was thankfully at sea level! As parents, we're always watching our kids for signs.

It's especially important to watch for warning signs in your kids when it comes to disordered eating. Always remind yourself that there's nothing wrong with you or your parenting if your kid needs help. You didn't cause the problem and can let go of any guilt or embarrassment you may be feeling because your primary job is to keep your child safe. Research shows that a whopping 80% of disordered eating stems from biological factors, and none of us has the privilege of choosing our DNA. In addition to a strong genetic component, there's often high participation in sports, a high achieving personality, high anxiety, and perfectionism, which can all trigger a child into a calorie deficit which is often the start of an eating disorder, according to researcher Gwenyth Olwyn.

Here are some of the most common warning signs to watch for in your kid:

1. Restricting particular foods or food groups.
2. A fear of eating foods with fat or sugar or those higher in calories.
3. Lack of enjoyment around food or foods that used to bring joy.
4. Agitation around meal times, skipping meal times, or a change in how your kid talks about food, particularly labeling foods as "good" or "bad."
5. Playing with food, using napkins to hide food (or giving food to family pets), or spending a lot of time in the bathroom after meals.

6. An increased preoccupation with their body, especially selfies.
7. A change in clothing, especially baggy or loose-fitting clothes.
8. An increased amount of movement.
9. Preoccupation with apps, trackers, or watches that log steps, miles, and calories.
10. If your child is assigned female at birth, late period onset or missed periods.
11. Thinning hair or brittle nails.
12. Mood swings.

Please reach out to your physician for a referral for your kid to both a dietitian and a psychologist if you sense your child has an eating disorder.

Unfortunately, many people have a preconceived notion that eating disorders only affect white, middle, to upper-class girls, and nothing could be farther from the truth. Eating disorders happen across all ages, genders, socioeconomic statuses (remember that not enough food can happen through restriction and also through poverty or lack of access), body sizes, and races. A kid labeled "overweight" or "obese" (I keep these words in quotes as the medical community has used these terms to pathologize people in larger bodies) can be just as susceptible to an eating disorder as someone who looks emaciated.

While it's crucial for you to understand that parents don't cause eating disorders, they can greatly impact a kid's beliefs around food and body, which can lead a kid to diet. Dieting alone is the number one predictor in the development of an eating disorder. The National Eating Disorders Association found that 35% of dieting becomes obsessive, and 20 to 25% of those diets turn into eating disorders. It can also be really difficult for a kid with disordered eating to recover if their parents exhibit abnormal behavior or beliefs around food.

What if your kid develops or has disordered eating? While there's a lot of inaccurate information about disordered eating, we do know many truths about anorexia nervosa. This list was produced in collaboration with Dr. Cynthia Bulik, Ph.D., FAED and the Academy for Eating Disorders, and it's important to share.

Truth #1: Many people with eating disorders look healthy yet may be extremely ill.

Truth #2: Families are not to blame and can be the patients' and providers' best allies in treatment.

Truth #3: An eating disorder diagnosis is a health crisis that disrupts personal and family functioning.

Truth #4: Eating disorders are not choices but serious biologically influenced illnesses.

Truth #5: Eating disorders affect people of all genders, ages, races, ethnicities, body shapes and weights, sexual orientations, and socioeconomic statuses.

Truth #6: Eating disorders carry an increased risk for both suicide and medical complications.

Truth #7: Genes and environment play important roles in the development of eating disorders.

Truth #8: Genes alone do not predict who will develop eating disorders.

Truth #9: Full recovery from an eating disorder is possible. Early detection and intervention are important.

If your child does develop an eating disorder, having a solid relationship with your body and your attitudes around food will undoubtedly positively impact your child's recovery. In fact, I'll go so far as to say that YOU must do the work to heal your relationship with food and your body before you try to pass along any of this information to your kid. Kids are incredibly smart, and they will see what you do much more than they will hear what you say.

You may want to look into FBT or family-based treatment providers in your area as they are very often considered the gold standard for therapeutic treatment. Two other great resources for families are FEAST (https://www.feast-ed.org/) and the National Eating Disorders Association (https://www.nationaleatingdisorders.org/).

* * *

SUMMARY

Be aware of disordered eating signs in your child/teen/young adult. These signs are not to be ignored, and the sooner you can get your child help through a treatment team, the better. Recognize your shame and guilt voice, as it will likely emerge, and kindly ask that voice to stay quiet while you prioritize the safety of your kid. There's no point in blaming yourself for your kid's problems. Now is the time for you to be your child's advocate and leader and help them into recovery.

* * *

- Getting help is actually a sign of strength.
- My job is to keep my child safe, and right now, they're showing signs that they might be unsafe and I want to help them.
- I'm a good parent with a good kid who is struggling and needs help.

Talking to Your Kid's Teacher/Coach About Food

My son came home from his first day of school, and I cheerfully asked, "How was your lunch?!" To me it felt like an easy conversation starter for a quick win. Lunch is always great, right?

"Not good, Mommy. They told me I couldn't eat my cookie first, so I only ate half."

My heart literally sank to the floor like a deflated balloon past its party prime. I wanted to shout noooooooooo!!

"I'm so sorry, buddy. How did you feel about that?" I asked.

"Not good because I wanted my cookie."

"Don't worry. Mommy is going to talk with your teachers and remind them that it's okay for you to choose the order that you want to eat your food and ask them to let you decide how much food you want to eat. It's okay to eat any food I pack for you."

Teaching kids they can't trust themselves or make their own choices around food can be really impactful on their emotions and damaging to their relationship with food in the long run.

From a young age, we want to encourage kids to listen to their bodies because only THEY know what feels good to THEM. As parents, we'd like to think we know what's best for our children, but we're also constantly reminded that our kids are their own person with their own unique desires and wants. Do we still offer them a variety of foods, including fruits and vegetables? Yes! Do we dictate what they should eat and rank foods into right and wrong or good and bad categories? No!

Picture this COVID times lunch scenario: Kids yelling around you, there's constant noise from the unzipping of lunchboxes and the clanging of water bottles onto desktops, you're starving since it's been over 4 hours since you last ate a meal because you didn't like the morning snack, yet you're eager to talk with your friends since wearing a mask 24/7 at school is hard, and this welcome break makes it easier to talk. Your little brain is processing so much emotionally and academically. Your time is limited to eat, and you might be feeling like you just want to go home. You may only like certain textures and flavors of foods, too, and desire something that feels soothing or comforting in some way, but it's too hard to pack those things without a microwave or toaster on hand. When you finally start eating, your teacher comes up to you and tells you to stop eating what you're eating and to eat something else instead. How would you feel if this was you?

Kids are very smart and may very well opt to eat the highest carb/sugar item first for a quick hit of energy. That makes complete sense. Do you wish your child would also eat the protein-packed main item you packed? Sure! You know this combination will help them get through their afternoon, but your child will know in time what works. You can ask your child if they feel hungry in the afternoon and encourage them to have the foods with higher staying power, but ultimately, it's up to your child to decide.

If you need a little help talking with your child's teacher or even their athletics coach, here's a script you can use from Katja Rowell,

M.D. "The Feeding Doctor." This genius script is succinct and powerful.

Hello!

Please allow _____ to decide how much to eat, and in what order, from what I have packed. Even if that means all they eat for lunch is "dessert," or if they start with dessert.

I trust that _____ can rely on hunger and fullness signals to know how much to eat. If they need help opening containers, I thank you for that. Otherwise, _____ should be good to go.

Please call my cell _____ if you have any questions.

Thank you for all you do for our children.

Parents, not schools, should be deciding what is appropriate for their child's lunch. Advocating for your child teaches them that they too can advocate for themselves. I believe that teachers and lunchroom helpers are coming from a place of concern and wanting to help, but too often their messaging is confusing for kids. I know teachers are doing the best with the information they have and often are simply following school or district policy that encourages kids to eat their "healthy" foods first, but the messaging can be damaging.

Our son's teacher was absolutely fine with him making his choices after that first day, and I would hope that your kid's teachers would also be open to the conversation. It's time we question why these "procedures" are in place and if they really benefit or hurt our kids.

I will say this gets trickier when your kid eats at the school cafeteria and you have no idea what they're eating. You can always check in with teachers and simply ask your child, "Are you getting enough to eat? Are there enough options at lunchtime?" Don't be surprised if your child comes home needing more of a meal than a snack after school. The lunch periods are usually very short and sometimes very early in the day, and there's overstimulation, which can very easily lead to under-consumption. I fully prepare for a post-school mini meal and always bring snacks in the car, despite being a very short drive from school.

The same is true for coaches who might be questioning after-school snacks your kid brings from home. Please advocate for your kid and let your coach know that you're working on finding the foods that give your kid the right amount of energy for practice. An apple might not do it; it might need to be a sandwich or granola bar or anything else that gives some quick energy during a very likely short time period between school and sports practice.

* * *

SUMMARY

Lunchtime at school can be tricky for kids. With limited time to eat, kids can feel pressured while eating in a high-stress and noisy lunch-room. It's important to let kids feel autonomous when it comes to decisions around food. Only your kid knows what tastes and feels best in their body and what will give them the energy they need in the moment. Of course, we can help kids understand what foods will help keep their energy levels sustained throughout the school day, too. Use the above script from "The Feeding Doctor" to communicate your desires with your kid's teacher and keep reminding your kid that they're in charge, which will feel like a refreshing position versus listening to teachers all day! Be prepared for your kid to eat another bigger snack or meal after school, as no matter how much we plan ahead, it's common that kids don't get their hunger needs met at either snack or lunch time because of a variety of factors.

* * *

Mantra

- My kid knows their body best.
- I trust my kid to trust themself.
- My job is to provide options I know my kid will like, and my kid can choose from there.
- I will have snacks ready for my kids after school as they'll very likely be hungry.

Section 6

Managing Relationships in the Age of Diet Culture

Surround Yourself with Body Positive Friends

The other night, my daughter asked me if I wanted to look at her bullet journal.

"Of course, I'd love to see it!"

She proudly showed me a list of her "highs" and "lows" for the day, her rating for the day, and a few things she was grateful for.

"That's really cool; I love it," I said, having to bite my tongue.

Never mind that I've been encouraging her to write in a journal before bedtime as a way to clear her mind and develop a gratitude practice for months, maybe even years.

"How did you come up with the idea?" I asked curiously.

"My friend is super into journaling right now."

Ahhh, yes, the power of friend influence, especially as a pre-teen, teen, and young adult, is very real. I'm incredibly grateful that I love our kids' friends, and they know that finding the right people to surround yourself with is important not only as a kid but also as an adult.

Did you know that research pins 95% of your success or failure in life on the people you habitually associate with? It's impossible to spend a lot of time with people and not have their opinions influence your mindset. If all your friends are counting calories, logging miles on their My Fitness Pal app, and ordering salads with dressing on the side while eating only a few bites, it's going to affect you in some way, big or small. And if you're constantly spending time with a life-long dieter, it's going to be hard not to let their thoughts about food and exercise seep into your conversations unless you set some solid boundaries.

One of the more challenging parts of this anti-diet journey is not only personally feeling like a sane person around food and your body but also finding other people who share your same goals and who will love and support you unconditionally. This is a tall order in a society where I'd argue the majority of women have dieted, don't like their bodies, or have some form of disordered/restrictive eating.

Think about the handful of people you spend the most time with and ask yourself these questions.

Does this person love and support me unconditionally?

Does this person bring up my weight or their weight in our conversations?

Does this person constantly comment or obsess about food?

Does this person say they worry about my size and want to help me lose weight? (See The Real Definition of Health.)

Did we bond over a group or specific diet in the past, like keto or our company's Biggest Loser annual competition?

Does this person constantly talk negatively about their or other people's body size?

Does this person actively diet (skip meals, pick at their food) during the time we spend together?

Do we have similar interests outside of the gym/movement classes?

Do I feel good about myself after spending time with them?

Would I want my kid to have a friend like this?

Giving real answers to these questions might make it obvious that it's time to distance yourself from certain people in your life. It's absolutely okay to end relationships that no longer serve you in a healthy way, and it's also okay to hold onto diet-filled relationships with some firmly laid boundaries, which I'll discuss in the next section. It can be difficult to let go of friendships and relationships, even if they're toxic.

Having a safety net of a few trusted family and friends can make all the difference in diet recovery. Show your kid what's important in a friendship, like having shared similar values and finding people who like/love you for who you are and encourage you to be your best self. Make sure your partner knows how to support you and can help share the right messages around food and body, too. Having mixed messages or even one parent with a damaging message can have a life-long negative effect on your kid. Reflect back on how many things stuck with you about food and body over the years that were said by parents, a family friend, or relative. Commit today to creating a safe space for yourself and your kid when it comes to food and body.

SUMMARY

Take some time to really evaluate who you spend your time with. Are these friends and family focused on food, body, and diet-related topics? Or are they focused on experiencing life together and able to love and support you unconditionally? It's important to have a "safe" network for yourself and your kids and to show them how to cultivate deep and meaningful relationships that don't center around dieting or body size.

* * *

Mantra

- I will surround myself with other anti-diet people.
- It's important to let go of toxic relationships that no longer serve me.
- I can set boundaries in relationships to protect myself and my kids.

Set Limits Around Friends or Family Who Fat Shame

"You've already had a lot of pasta. Are you sure you want more?"

This question came to my son at our dinner table from a non-immediate family member, and I quickly shot it down by reminding that person that he knows his body best and to please stop commenting on how much our kids eat at the table. We can never know what's happening inside another person's body, so how can we know when someone else has had enough to eat?

If you've been the recipient of a comment like this, you know how these questioning words can immediately send you into freakout mode about your ability to judge your hunger, your preferences, and how you're doing things "wrong," despite there not being a right or wrong way to "do" your food.

Maybe some of these comments sound familiar, too.

Are you sure you need that?

Those are so bad for you, aren't they?

Have you ever thought about going on a diet?

I have a great gym you should join.

I'm just so worried about your health.

Should you be giving your kid that much sugar?
Isn't that too much to put on your kid's plate?
You really need to lose some weight.

While these comments are well-meaning, they're fatphobic. As the saying goes, you can dress up a pig in lipstick, but a pig is still a pig. Comments that refer to other people's size, the amount of food they eat, and the movement they choose to participate in are all rooted in fatphobia and are inappropriate. While many family members, friends, or doctors in the medical community saying these comments don't know about HAES, their ignorance on the subject can be damaging.

Contrary to popular belief, studies fail to show that larger-bodied kids and teens eat more than their thinner peers. In fact, a study by Rocandio et al. showed that caloric and carbohydrate intake was significantly lower in so-called "overweight" students compared to non-"overweight" students. Another study by Shapiro et al. showed estimates of caloric intake and physical activity didn't correlate with body measurements in infants or kids. Our culture is filled with messages that bigger sized people got their body size from eating too much, yet these studies show us that our food intake isn't necessarily a size predictor.

Regardless of how much people eat, a significant concern is weight stigma. Fatphobic comments can cause people to feel shame and guilt and can even trigger disordered eating patterns. This is referred to as weight stigma, which is broadly defined as bias or discriminatory behaviors targeted at "overweight" and "obese" individuals because of their weight. Studies have shown that people who experience weight stigma can actually exhibit poorer health outcomes and that shaming people does NOT motivate them to lose weight.

Researcher and psychologist Rebecca Puhl reports that the effects of weight stigma can be real and long-lasting and include depression, anxiety, low self-esteem, disordered eating, weight gain, avoiding healthcare, and increased psychological stress. Christy Harrison, MPH, RD, CEDS shared a 2017 study that reported people with high levels of weight stigma had "twice the risk of high allostatic load—a measure of cumulative stress on the body systems—that puts people at greater risk for of Type 2 Diabetes, cardiovascular disease, and mortality." (Footnote 1) This is important because the study showed that weight stigma was an independent health risk factor, even when BMI was controlled for. This is critical to understand because it shows that weight stigma, not necessarily weight, can potentially account for many of the adverse health conditions that are seen in people with larger bodies.

Unfortunately, there's no way we can control what other people say or do. I wish I could wave a magic anti-diet wand for ending all diet talk, weight stigma, and shame around food and bodies. Until I find said magic wand, I recommend you become well-versed in how to set boundaries for yourself and teach your kids how to do the same. Remember boundaries are for you and not something you have to do. You might not feel like setting a boundary and choose to simply walk away, the situation might not feel safe to set a boundary, or you may end or interrupt an uncomfortable conversation to excuse yourself. All of these are perfectly okay options to choose. You need to feel pretty solid in your diet recovery to take a public stand, and it isn't your responsibility to speak up or educate others unless you're ready.

Sometimes the people saying these hurtful comments are our mothers, sisters, or close friends, and you want to maintain the rela-tionship and feel safe in your interactions. One of the best ways to do this is to set a boundary. It's important to note boundaries aren't the same thing as a threat. It's not a way to feel like you'll have the power to change the other person's behavior. Instead, it's a measure that you'll take in order to protect yourself.

In general, a boundary follows this formula: If you do X, then I will do Y. For example, if you choose to talk about weight, then I'll choose to leave your home/end this conversation/hang up the phone. You can also take the approach of simply stating your request: "I feel uncomfortable talking about food and body but really want to connect with you. Can we please talk about something else?" Or: "I'm working really hard to heal my relationship with food and my body, and right now, I can't have any conversations about that topic without feeling really triggered. I love spending time with you and know we can find so many other things to talk about." Or you can let the other person know you've really struggled with feeling good in your body, and participating in dieting has been really hurtful to you and caused you a lot of pain and suffering. If you can bring in a sense of humanity with your feelings, I doubt anyone will want argue with your feelings and want to respect your wishes.

Once you've stated your boundary, steer the conversation in a new direction: "I'm reading a great new book I'd love to tell you about." Or: "Did you see *Saturday Night Live* last week?" One final approach you can try is this: "You know what? I'm not comfortable discussing weight loss and dieting (or: "It's not okay to make comments about my body/my kid's body"), and I'd love to choose a new topic now, okay?"

Vinny Welsby, a fat activist and author (www.fiercefatty.com), gives great advice about fatphobia and boundaries. Their philosophy is to adopt these three words: remove, reduce, and protect. First, can you remove the source of fatphobia? End a relationship, unfollow on social media, or stop watching a TV show? If you can't do that, how can you reduce your exposure to a certain situation or person? Can you sit further away from them at family gatherings or cut your vacation time shorter? Can you set a boundary? Lastly, can you protect yourself by reaching out ahead of time and asking if this person could help you with something and explain how you've been negatively affected by diet culture and fatphobia? Can you protect yourself by practicing self-care or reminding yourself of your values and your resolve to stay out of diet talk before being in a situation that will likely be filled with conversations about food and body?

What about those unsolicited comments about your body, especially before, during, and after pregnancy? Fielding these comments can be challenging or triggering, especially if they involve weight you may have lost. It's normal to have that internal fist-pumping: "Yes, my jeans are a little looser." It's not your fault, as we've all been trained to view weight loss as a success and weight gain as a failure. In these instances, I find it's best to say that you don't focus on weight anymore, and you have genetics to thank for your size. Or find a way to steer the conversation in a new direction. If a friend is fishing for a compliment about their recent weight loss, you can simply say, "I think you're beautiful no matter what."

Ragen Chastain also has some great information about boundary setting with friends and physicians on her website. She makes the very important point that it isn't your job to educate anyone on the topic of HAES. Unless someone asks or wants to learn, I wouldn't recommend launching into your soapbox speech, although it's very tempting once you learn the truth.

SUMMARY

Research shows that weight stigma has a serious effect on our health. It's not okay for other people to comment on your food, your body size, or how much you move your body. Having a script ready in your pocket or knowing you can simply change, interrupt, or end an uncomfortable conversation is important. Boundaries follow this simple formula: If you do X, then I will do Y. Practice boundary setting with friends, family, or physicians. Think about how you can remove, reduce, and protect yourself when it comes to interacting with fatphobic individuals or media content. You don't have to educate another person about what you know unless they ask and want to learn.

* * *

MANTRA

- I will not let other people comment on my food or my body.
- Boundary setting is a way for me to protect myself.
- It's okay to remove, reduce, and protect myself when it comes to hurtful interactions with people in my life.

Reflect on Your Role Models

Who do you admire and why? That was the question my daughter had to answer for her English essay. I love these thought-provoking questions that help kids see the true essence of people beyond their outward appearance. It's easy to get wrapped up in the day-to-day momentum and forget to step back and think about what and who matters to you and why.

Pretend you're back in school for the day, and your assignment is to write down five people in your life who you most admire. Next to their name, write down one or two reasons *why* you admire them. Perhaps they showed or taught you bravery, courage, kindness, resilience, or forgiveness. Perhaps they've done something interesting with their career, or they've done something to help other people in a big or small way. Once you've completed your list, look back and see how many reasons had anything to do with their body shape or size. I'm willing to bet your answer is zero.

Doing this exercise can be a powerful reminder of what's truly important to you and what kind of legacy you want to leave behind for your own family. Do you want them to remember you as the one googling gluten-free cake recipes for your birthday cake until 11:30 p.m. (unless, of course, there's a real celiac diagnosis)?

In the next space, take the time to write out your top 10 to 20 values. How do you want to spend your days? Where do you want to focus your energy? If you were looking back at your life on your 85th birthday, what do you want to have accomplished?

None of us knows how much time we have on this planet.

There's no amount of cottage cheese, chia seeds, or baked chicken that will guarantee you'll make it to 65, 85, or 100 years old. There's no magic body size that's guaranteed to be disease free.

No magic code exists.

"I wish I had eaten more lettuce and dieted more," said no one EVER in their final days.

The wish is usually about having done and tried things that brought joy, more connection, more adventure, and more love.

Maybe one of the people you admire lived with that certain zest, a positive attitude or *je ne sais quoi*. It's never too late to become the person you want to be.

Inhabit your body with aliveness and passion. Give yourself permission to NOT be known as "the healthy one." I realize it might feel scary to let go of an identity that you clung to for years or decades, but it's even scarier to live a life fighting against your body and treating her or your kid in a cruel way because of your or their size. It's never too late to be true to yourself and create the most honest version of yourself.

Trust yourself.

What if you could surrender and let go of trying to control things outside of your control (yes, this means your body size)? What else would become important to you?

What if you could let your food and body be what they want to be?

What if you spent less time "fixing" and more time cultivating fierce self-love and even fiercer self-acceptance?

What would happen if you adopted a sense of hopelessness instead of hope around diets? If you believed there wasn't a solution and nothing worked, what else could you spend your time hoping for instead? Sometimes the best thing to do is give up, especially when it comes to an industry with an almost zero success rate.

What does it look like for you to connect with your body and give her comfort? How can you find ways to embrace your unique beauty?

Do what (and go where) your heart calls, and don't worry about what other people might think. Sing. Dance. Laugh.

As Mary Oliver says, "Tell me, what is it you plan to do with your one wild and precious life?"

* * *

SUMMARY

It can be really easy to lose sight of what we truly care about and admire in other people. We're constantly bombarded with images that promote the thin ideal, so it's no wonder we're trying to obtain this in our own lives. Instead of chasing the impossible, I recommend giving up hope that some magic formula to permanently and safely change your body exists. When you stop and think about it, what you really admire and appreciate about others has nothing to do with their size. Get curious about what you appreciate in others and cultivate your own values list, which can be an incredibly important anchor as you wade through diet culture's waters. How do you want to spend your precious time?

MANTRA

- I'm becoming more myself every day.
- I'm making choices that align with my values.
- I can be hopeless about diets and hope for things that are actually attainable.
- I appreciate, admire, respect, and care for others regardless of their size.

Appreciate Non-Size-Related Things About Yourself

There was a time not too long ago when it was really easy for me to see all the things my partner and kids did that got under my skin. Everywhere I turned, there was some audacious crime that would undermine my efforts, big and small. I felt like my background noise was more nails on a chalkboard than Mozart as I went about my days. It was easy to focus on what was going wrong in our house because something was always "wrong." After unsuccessfully trying to control my family's behavior (we can't ever control someone else's actions), I decided I was the person who needed to change. But how was *I* going to change when *they* just needed to pick up their dirty clothes?

I turned to the happiness pros, who almost unanimously recommended one simple thing to do every day. Enter the gratitude journal. Cost-free and as easy as putting pen to paper in 5 minutes or less. Sounded simple enough and worth a try, especially now that I understood finding happiness was an inside job and not one I could assign to anybody else in our family but me. After just a few days, I noticed

I was looking for and appreciating things that brought even the simplest gratitude.

Has it been life-changing? Maybe. Do I go to bed happier every night after reflecting on things that I'm grateful for? Yes. Have I missed a night since I started? Not many, and if I do, I mentally count out at least five moments of gratitude. Do I still find half-eaten apples next to dirty socks crumpled in the backseat of the car? Yes. Does finding them send me on a one-way ticket down the rabbit hole of despair? No.

Let's be real, my kids forget to do their homework, make their bed, flush the toilet, take out the trash, and brush their teeth. The list of things they miss sometimes goes on longer than a CVS receipt. Despite my frustration, I want to look for the things my kids are doing that make my heart melt, like the sight of a 9-week-old puppy or newborn baby. A little hand squeeze, a hug, a shared laugh, a sweet comment, or nighttime cuddle. These are the moments I want to remember, and these are the things helping me find my happiness now. The biggest bonus is I didn't even need my spouse or kids to change in order to feel happy. This doesn't mean I don't ask my family to do their chores or clean up after themselves; it just means I can approach the ask with an attitude of gratitude versus The Grinch.

This reminds me of how little we play this same game with ourselves. Do you constantly look for the good in yourself or focus on the negative? How many times do you walk by the mirror and slump inside after catching your reflection? Maybe a better question would be, do you even look in the mirror, or do you purposefully avoid looking at yourself? How many times do you have something nice to say about yourself when you're brushing your teeth or getting dressed? What would it feel like for you to recognize the person beneath the skin in the mirror? Would it be hard for you to see something beautiful?

Beauty is a word that's been co-opted by the diet industry to have a very narrow definition. What if you made up a new definition that you could enter into the urban dictionary? Could you see your reflection beyond the mirror into all the challenges you've overcome, all the things you've accomplished, all the days you've shown up when you didn't feel like it, and given yourself a smile?

Mel Robbins's book, *The High 5 Habit*, suggests that a simple high five in the mirror every morning can be just the physical cue you need to feel better about yourself. Cheesy? Yes. But the fundamental idea is as solid as the three pigs' brick house. Acknowledging you're here with a sense of "I see you, and I've got you" is really powerful.

Maybe you don't need a high five or a smile, but pay attention to your inner critic and make sure you like what you hear. If you don't, let your critic know you heard them, but you don't believe them, won't listen to them, and give them the fingers in the ear treatment while you shout "la, la, la, la!" Immature? Yes, but finding ways to quiet your unreasonable voice is welcome. Another way to stop critical chatter is by talking to yourself the same way you'd talk with a friend in your same situation. You'd never say, "You're right, your body is hideous and nobody is going to love you." You'd give your friend a boost of confidence by reminding them of all their great qualities. It turns out that we're much better at giving advice to our friends than ourselves, so cultivate a sense of friendship with yourself to give better advice.

I believe there's beauty in every single body, just like there's always a beautiful flower waiting inside a spring bud to come into full bloom. It's an indisputable truth. You might not notice the details of a fresh bud or the colors peeking out from their tight petal cocoon, but this doesn't mean beauty isn't waiting to uncurl into perfection. When flowers do come into bloom in a garden, it's not one particular flower that makes the garden beautiful—it's all the different colors, shapes, textures, and sizes of the flowers together that make us stop in our tracks to take in all the beauty. Our human brain has just been trained to see one image as beautiful: a white, thin (with curves in all the right places), cisgender, able-bodied woman. This image has been airbrushed into our psyche, yet less than 5% of the population naturally falls into this waif-like model category.

I started thinking more about what I wanted to see as beautiful. One day I was looking at a picture of my nana and her sisters-in-law, who were the beloved matriarchs of our family, from one of our family picnics. Something about this picture made me stop and really think about my roots. Even though I look at a picture of my nana almost daily, I really looked at her in a different way this time.

I thought about my nana and papa and how hard they worked, how much they sacrificed, and how my papa came to America through Ellis Island and sponsored his sisters to come on different occasions. I thought about how my nana worked at a young age and only went back to finish high school because a truant officer found out she was skipping school to work. I thought about how she opened her own catering business and ran it successfully with no college education while raising four kids. And then I saw her strong arms and legs, her soft belly, her welcoming eyes, and her enormous heart.

I also thought about my other grandma, who was brave enough to have my dad at age 18. I thought about how she handled divorce, single motherhood, and another divorce and is still going strong at 96 years old. I thought about my grandpa, who served our country and fought a hard battle against cancer.

I thought about my parents' grandparents and their parents. I thought about my mom being the first female to graduate from college, raise two kids, work full time, and go back to school for a master's degree so she could eventually become a principal, all while my dad worked two jobs. I traced back my roots near and far and felt enormous gratitude. Their experiences are woven into my DNA, and my body size and shape are largely passed on from each of them. So much of what women experience today is pressure to be thin, to be somebody that maybe isn't in their genetic cards. How many times have you heard, "You don't want to end up looking like Granny or Gramps or Auntie or Uncle."

So instead of fighting to be a shape I'm not, I want to look back at where I've come from and feel proud and grateful for who has come before me. I want to end up looking like the ancestors I'm proud to call my own. They made countless sacrifices so I could be alive. I don't want to spend my precious time fighting for something that doesn't matter and takes me further away from who I'm meant to be.

This week, take a few minutes and find some pictures of your ancestors. Have a moment of appreciation for what they did so you could be here. Be grateful for your roots. Let this inspire you as you write a list of 25 things you appreciate about your body that have nothing to do with your size. Here are just a few things to consider...

Your heart, lungs, kidneys, and other internal organs are constantly working to keep you alive. Your arms let you hug your loved ones, your legs get you where you want to go, your eyes let you soak in the sunset hues I like to refer to as rainbow time, and your ears allow you to hear your kid call your name or the birds greeting a sunny day. How about your sense of purpose that motivates you, your great sense of humor, your ability to make other people smile, or your solid determination?

If you decide to pick up the habit of writing in a gratitude journal, why not add one thing a day that you appreciate about yourself? Imagine having a list of 365 things that you like about yourself by the end of the year. You might find that your background music changes from scary horror movie to light-hearted rom-com.

Keeping this list handy and even sharing it with your children just might encourage you to smile back at yourself, reach for a high five, and quiet that inner critic the next time you look in the mirror.

* * *

SUMMARY

Trying to live up to diet culture's definition of beauty will leave you constantly falling short and finding what's "wrong"" with your body instead of seeking to find things about yourself that you like and appreciate. You get to decide what beauty means for yourself. Find pictures of your ancestors and take time to soak in where and who you've come from. Get out some paper and make a list of 25 things you like about yourself outside of your appearance. Experiment with writing in a gratitude journal by writing five things that you appreciate everyday.

* * *

MANTRA

- Beauty is more than skin deep.
- I can create my own definition of beautiful.
- Outside of my physical characteristics, what do I like about myself?
- I will practice gratitude daily.

Watch What You Say

I used to do this all the time.

"Wow! You look great. You've lost so much weight! What's your secret?"

As a Pilates and yoga instructor for the past two decades, it's almost been my job to acknowledge these seemingly heroic changes in my clients.

I hear moms all the time commenting to other moms, saying, "Ohhhh, you look so skinny! You look amazing!" "Have you seen her lately? She's lost so much weight!" "I can't believe you were pregnant just two weeks ago!" The verbal high five, slap on the back, atta girl words of praise.

Years ago, those kinds of compliments would fuel me to work even harder to maintain my "perfect physique," so I'd continue to receive compliments from friends, family, clients, or strangers—a sign that I was "winning" or "succeeding" in some way. I would dole out those kinds of compliments to other people, too. It was like the fellow dieters were part of a secret society of sorts, acknowledging and confirming each other for our dutiful efforts.

I now realize the extraordinary amount of pressure that weight-related compliments place on people. Praising someone's appearance might *seem* like an encouraging, supportive, or nice thing to do—but it's really not.

Why?

Firstly, you don't know how—or why—your loved one has lost weight.

Let's say you notice that someone's body has changed. Her cheekbones are more defined. Her waistline is smaller. She has lost weight! You immediately begin heaping praise on her. But hold on a sec—maybe she lost weight because she's grieving a devastating loss in her life, like the death of a loved one, an ugly breakup or divorce, and has lost her appetite due to grief. Maybe she's battling cancer. Maybe she has a serious gastrointestinal disease. Maybe she has developed an eating disorder, like anorexia, bulimia, or orthorexia. Maybe she's a survivor of sexual assault or rape and has lost weight due to PTSD. You're praising someone for how "great" they look when she might be going through a horrific ordeal.

Or maybe she lost weight because she went on a diet. Well, diets almost *never* lead to long-term weight loss. Very few people (almost none, basically unicorns) can maintain diet-induced weight loss for a period of 2 to 5 years or longer. The rare unicorns who can usually do so at the expense of their mental sanity—they're completely obsessed with food and food-related thoughts. By praising someone for going on a diet, you're heaping additional pressure on their shoulders to keep off the weight they've lost, which is virtually impossible. It also gives the person pause as they wonder, "Geez, I really must have looked bad or unacceptable before I lost weight." Before you praise someone for losing weight, stop and consider how your words might harm them.

The next time you see a friend or family member, try giving a compliment that has *nothing* to do with their weight. For example:

"You're so creative. I love how your mind works."

"You're hysterical! You should seriously do stand-up comedy."

"I admire the way you parent your kids. You're so nurturing and patient."

"I love how you're always doing spontaneous things—like packing up and taking a road trip at the last minute. You inspire me!"

When talking with a child, instead of saying you're so pretty, ask the child, "What's your favorite book?" or "What's your favorite subject in school?" or "What do you love doing after school?" Or simply say, "I've missed you!" or "It's great to see you. How are you doing?" And really listen to their answers.

Because in the end, being heard—and being seen for who you truly are on the inside, not the outside—is so much more valuable than receiving superficial praise about your body. Text a non-weight-related compliment to your best friend right now. Find someone in your household with whom you can do the same. Let's create a world where "oh my gosh, you look so skinnnnnnnny!" is no longer considered the highest form of praise.

What happens if you find yourself stuck in a weight praising conversation party? Simply steering the conversation in a new direction with a subject change, like dishing about your favorite book or TV show, can be really effective. If that doesn't work or you don't feel like you have the energy to redirect the conversation, you can simply walk away. If a friend is fishing for compliments on their weight loss, you can say, "I think you look great no matter what!" and move on to a new topic.

* * *

SUMMARY

Next time you're tempted to comment on someone's weight loss, pause. Take a moment and think about how you can connect with this person outside of their size. Because we don't know the history or reasoning behind a change in body size, coupled with the fact that weight loss with diets is almost guaranteed to be temporary, it's best to focus on topics outside of weight. Compliment your friend or loved one on their personality, their creativity, or their leadership at work or in the community. If you've been the recipient of weight-based compliments, really think about how these messages affected you. Did you feel good about your size prior to these compliments? Did you feel shame when your body changed? Did you feel pressure to "keep up" your dieting tactics that were really causing you mental and/or physical harm?

MANTRA

- I can find new ways to recognize friends and loved ones outside of their size.
- I love and care about people for who they are, not what they look like.
- I can find beauty in all shapes and sizes.

Make Your Own Values

What is your number one pursuit in life?

Is it to finally get that "perfect" or "ideal" or "better" body? Is it to achieve that "beach body" by June first?

That was my number one pursuit for a long time, I'm embarrassed to admit. Year after year, I sat down with my journal and pen on New Year's Day to write out some slightly nuanced version of the same weight loss goal. Eat clean! Exercise more! Only eat organic foods! Be more mindful when eating! Eat out less!

Cultivating the ideal physique—which in my mind, was long, lean, toned, and sculpted—was one of my top priorities in life. It's staggering how much time I spent trying to create "that body."

If I were to tally it all up, how much time would it be? A thousand hours? Ten thousand? A hundred thousand? A stupefying amount of time! Worse yet, in these wasted hours, I also lost a sense of what was truly important to me. What did I want to focus on? What really mattered to me? How would it look to live a life according to my values instead of according to diet culture's empty promises that never really got me "there" anyway?

Dieting itself can become an identity that's not only hard to shed, but hard to remove to really see what's underneath, just like a precious fossil waiting to be discovered by the right hands. I used to believe that my value was as intertwined with my size as a pile of newborn puppies. Health is still a value of mine, but that picture of health is from a completely weight-neutral place and has nothing to do with my size.

Today, I choose to spend my time differently. I have different values and pursuits:

1. Dependability: I want to be a great mama to my six kids.
2. Love: I want my family, especially my kids, to feel my immense LOVE for them every day.
3. Growth: I want to be constantly learning and growing as a human.
4. Friendship: I want to make time for relationships and be the best friend to my family and my friends.
5. Education: I want to write books and share my ideas and stories. I want to coach, teach, and help women give up dieting for good, so they have time to do things that are truly meaningful for them and help them teach their kids to do the same. I want to share my message in schools, too, and help kids learn about health and how to manage their mental health.
6. Health: I want to take good care of myself and feel healthy and strong—without worrying or obsessing about my size.
7. Connection: I want to be connected to and make a difference in my community and be of service to as many people as I can.
8. Spirituality: I want to make time for faith and spiritual connection.

9. Adventure: I want to have adventures in my local 'hood and out in the world.
10. Kindness/Achievement: I want to die one day knowing that I made a difference in people's lives. It doesn't have to be "one million people," and I don't have to be "world-famous" necessarily, but knowing that I helped a few people be happier and healthier, to feel more freedom and joy…that's enough.

Those are just 10 of my pursuits in life. I have PLENTY others, too. But getting a "perfect summer bikini beach body" (whatever the heck that even means since putting a swimsuit on anybody makes it a bikini body!) is NO LONGER on my list of pursuits or values. THANK THE LORD FOR THAT. I am so grateful that nowadays I have pursuits that are bigger than "weight loss." And I know you do, too.

Your turn.

What are your biggest, most precious, most important pursuits in life? If you weren't spending every waking minute scrutinizing your meal plan and tracking your steps, where would you focus? Answering the question "wouldn't it be great if I could…" might help steer you in the right direction.

What's on your list? Get out paper and pen and jot down your first value today!

* * *

SUMMARY

Dieting takes up an enormous amount of time and energy. In addition to lost time, it's also very easy to lose your sense of self. It's easy to lose sight of your true values because those often need to get ignored or covered up in order to meet any diet's unrealistic goals, measures, and metrics. I encourage you to take some time to think about what your true values are in life. How do you want to live if not in accordance with diet culture's rules? Grab some paper and pen and jot down what's important. Is it connection, freedom, adventure, family, growth, compassion, honesty, and kindness that you want to focus on?

* * *

MANTRA

- I want to live life according to my own values.
- Living life according to my values means more than any number on the scale.
- Letting go of what I thought was important opens up my life for things that really matter.

Section 7

Caring for Your Body

Move Your Body for Joy, Not Punishment

I used to literally count out my daily caloric intake and offset a decent amount of that intake with activity. I've blocked out the exact counterbalance that I thought was "acceptable," but I remember it was a careful calculation. This wasn't hard for me because I've always been active and love to move. I think I get this gene from my dad, who's constantly tinkering and working on a project inside the house or out in the yard to this day in his late 70s.

The difference between the way I move now versus back then is I really love the movement I do. I listen to my body. I take days of rest and know that if I can't or don't want to move, it won't be the end of the world, won't affect my body size or determine my worth or value as a person. I don't pick an activity based on the calories I burn anymore. I pick an activity based on what my heart desires.

Do you tie your or your kid's food intake to how much activity you get?

Do any of these thoughts sound familiar?

If I eat this today, I'll go for a long run tomorrow.

I was so bad yesterday, so today, I have to take that HIIT spin class to burn it off.

I can't stop eating the entire bag of chips, so I'm going to punish myself with extra gym time this week.

Ugh, my stomach is so big, I have to double down on my workouts STAT.

So many of us have been conditioned that exercise should be used as a form of punishment, a way to make up for the food we've eaten, or a way to show our body who's boss. How many times did you calculate your daily caloric intake only to promise to counter your intake with exercise? For me, the word exercise conjures up images of polyester gym shorts and Reebok step risers along with an attitude of force, which is why I prefer to use the word movement instead of exercise.

With a childhood filled with dance, a degree in kinesiology or exercise physiology, and two decades as a movement instructor, you'd be hard-pressed to find someone more passionate about movement than me. For me, movement feels like medicine and a truly sacred practice where I can connect with myself and experience a sense of freedom, peace, and joy. My weekly yoga classes that I teach are the place where I reconnect body and mind and fill up my spiritual, emotional, and physical cup. With that said, it's important to know that movement is not a requirement for anyone, isn't always possible for everyone because of any number of barriers, and is never a measure of someone's worth, value, or health. Ragen Chastain says that "a Netflix marathon and running a marathon have the same value."

What about taking movement too far? Do you know if you exercise normally? Abnormally? Excessively? Do you sense you have an addiction to movement? How can you know? Researcher Gwyneth Olywn has a useful guide to knowing whether you are a normal or abnormal exerciser. Here are two major signs of a normal exerciser:

1. They take adequate rest to heal an injury.
2. They consume adequate calories to sustain peak energy.

Someone who is addicted to exercise will exhibit the following:

1. They feel the need to do more in order to get the same desired feeling or "high."
2. They desire to participate in exercise activities over spending time with family or friends.
3. They feel agitated if friends/family express concern and a return to the exercise at an even higher intensity.
4. They feel anxious if they're unable to exercise.
5. They feel the need to plan the next event as soon as the last one is finished, constantly thinking about exercise more than anything else.
6. They feel like they're suffering without it. It becomes the most important thing in their life.

In relation to overdoing exercise, an important topic to discuss is the female triad. For those of you with daughters, please be on the lookout for signs that point to your daughter exhibiting all three of these traits: inadequate intake, loss of period, and loss of bone density. Busy teens can easily mask this combination, so it's very important to make sure your athletic teens are getting adequate food and rest.

As I mentioned earlier, it's VERY important if you are actively recovering from an eating disorder or even subclinical eating disorder to give your body a period of rest. This is crucial for allowing your body to come back into energy balance and eliminate the deficit that has been there with any amount of restriction (even if the amount of restriction seems insignificant to you). Once your body has weight restored (put loosely, this is the weight you are when you aren't trying to interfere with your food) and your energy levels are stable (this is very individualized for everyone), you can resume activities.

I believe that movement is a gift you give yourself versus the diet mentality of using movement to lose weight or burn calories. When done appropriately, movement can heal; it can be a great source of stress relief, fuel for creativity, improve your mood and sleep, increase your energy, aid in digestion, and be a way to feel proud of yourself. Remember that movement doesn't have to come from a gym membership. Movement can be found in a walk around the block, folding laundry and taking the stairs as you put everything away, or sweeping the floor. We often move our bodies a lot more than we think!

As you reassess your relationship with movement, ask yourself these important questions:

Can I view movement as something I do for and not against myself?

Can I communicate to my children that moving my body feels good and is a way to feel strong and be able to take care of myself and my kids?

How can I find ways to get our whole family to move together?

What would feel good for my body?

If I knew that my body size wouldn't change, what would I enjoy doing the most?

If my time is very limited, how can I add in small movements throughout my day to bring my heart rate up, even for a couple of minutes?

Can I recognize my value without needing an external badge of movement completion?

It can be helpful to think about if you want to have any goals outside of weight loss when it comes to movement. As a Pilates instructor, I focused on four core areas with my clients: strength, stability, stretch, and stamina. Think about what ways you want to improve your quality of life, and find ways to develop these skills over time. Working on making daily tasks easier, like not getting winded walking up a flight of stairs, is just as worthy a goal as running your first 5K!

Lastly, look to your kids for inspiration. They're natural movers. I think about our boys who ask me to chase them in the morning to brush their hair and are still running laps up to the second we turn out the lights at night. They certainly don't tie movement as necessary to eat certain foods. Think more like your kids, and do any movements that spark joy, a la Marie Kondo. Search for color changing leaves or sea glass on the beach, walk the dog, play hide and go seek with your family, hunt for uniquely shaped rocks, or ride your bike. And remember, searching for shows and spending the day on the couch watching them is always an option, too.

* * *

SUMMARY

Instead of thinking about exercise (aka movement) as a way to punish yourself for what you ate on any given day, week, or month, see if you can reclaim a connection to your body through movement. What feels good for your body? What brings you joy? What would you do if you knew that your body size wouldn't change because of your participation in any particular activity? Remember that movement doesn't need to come from a fancy gym membership. Activities around the house or a walk around the block can all be great ways to experience joyful movement. Even turning up the music and having a dance party in your kitchen counts!

* * *

MANTRA

- Moving my body is not an obligation.
- I move my body only in ways that bring joy and not pain, pleasure and not punishment.
- I can find many ways to move my body.
- I can enjoy days when my body calls for rest.

Stop Using Fitness Trackers

For months, my son begged me for a fitness watch.

"Mom, literally EVERYONE in my class has one. Aaaaand, EVERYONE has their own iPad, too. C'mon, Mom, pleeeeeease."

"Wow, that's a lot of kids with devices," I replied, unshaken.

"Mom, please, why can't I have it? You're sooooo mean!"

My answer continued to be a hard no. I didn't want him to rely on some external factor to "track" how much he should be doing or how much he wasn't doing.

Relying on outside factors to reinforce your self-esteem or "prove" your worth isn't a great idea. When you start relying on outside factors, you lose your sense of self, the ability to connect with your body's true desires, and very often miss important messages or feelings from your body. As an adult, it's not uncommon to reach for an app, a watch, a plan, or a scale in order to avoid feeling difficult feelings or as a way to gain a sense of control. Dieting or tracking is often the coping mechanism of choice, especially if you have any previous experience with dieting.

Do you find that you constantly "track" your progress or make sure that you get in your 10,000 steps daily? While there's nothing wrong with being physically active and moving your body, it can become problematic if you're looking to outside sources to tell you when you've had "enough" or when you can "stop." Sometimes you might find yourself reaching for these outside tools during times of stress. When you feel the pull to "check" yourself, check inside first and see if there might be another stressor prompting this outside approval. Perhaps you choose not to move your body and schedule time to talk with a trusted friend or therapist. Perhaps you want to move your body *and* call a friend, or practice some deep breaths or write in a journal or watch something on Netflix.

A question I always like to ask clients to consider about movement is; *If body size didn't matter in our culture and if moving your body didn't even burn calories, what would you decide to do because you really wanted to?* Maybe some days you'll feel like a short walk, some days you'll feel like jogging, some days you'll feel like yoga or Pilates, some days you'll feel like playing tag with your kids, and other days your body is calling you to rest and enjoy stillness. The goal is to keep checking within, not looking at an app or tracker to determine how much and when you need to move in order to prove your worth or health.

Apps and trackers can also be anxiety-provoking, which is the last thing anxiety-prone disordered eaters need! In general, kids seem to be dealing with a lot more anxiety these days, so doing anything we can to diminish additional anxiety-provoking activities is important. There's one way around this for kids who really want devices with trackers. When we got our older girls Apple watches, we had them turn their fitness tracker off. Young kids do NOT need to be tracking their movement. They innately want to move for pure joy and fun and are bouncing with energy throughout the day. Don't forget, busy mamas, you're getting so much built-in movement during the day caring for young kids and your home (the laundry and cooking alone!). Moving your body doesn't have to involve tennis shoes and a gym membership. All movement counts and matters.

Look at your child's sense of pure joy for movement to find inspiration to move, and ignore the statistics and numbers that supposedly give you a measure of your steps along with your worth. Let go of counting 10,000 steps and you just might find that you feel like you have 10,000 more moments to breathe, be in the moment, and find inspiration in your brain that's been freed from constant counting and tracking.

* * *

SUMMARY

Fitness watches and tracking apps might seem like a great idea to "make sure" you're "tracking" your daily activity levels, but they're very often another dieting tool to measure your worth against. In seeking assurance or guidance from any outside source, you can lose touch with your own body's desires and needs for not only movement but rest. Instead of you or your kid using these devices, take a pause when you find the pull toward these items and ask yourself if there's a difficult feeling or situation you may be avoiding. Ask yourself what else might be stressful in your life. Ask yourself what other coping mechanisms you could utilize instead of a tracker. Ideas include deep breathing, calling a friend, making an appointment with a therapist, or asking for help from family or friends in areas where you need support.

* * *

Mantra

- I will listen to my body to know how much movement (if any) feels right.
- On any given day, my body wants to do different movement or no movement at all.
- I don't need an app or watch to tell me how much is enough for my body.
- I will focus on internal and not external cues when it comes to moving my body.

Give Up Control and Perfection

To show his disgust about not getting the sticker he wanted after getting his flu shot, my son did something that figuratively pushed me flat against the elevator wall like one of those spin-until-you-toss-your-cookies rides at Great America. He was so mad that he chose to bend down and literally lick the elevator floor at the DOCTOR'S OFFICE (you know, the place with more germs than you care to think about). Talk about the worst nightmare for me, a self-prescribed, medium-to-high germaphobe depending on whether I'm in Target or in an airport bathroom.

Once I peeled myself off the side of the elevator and the other kids had all covered their mouths in horror, I stood there frozen like Elsa in the depths of Ahtohallan. There wasn't a wipe, Band-Aid, hand sanitizer, or mouthwash that could fix the situation. The damage had been done. I took a deep breath and prepared myself to view the welcome sign to Stomachfluville in the very near future.

Guess what? My son didn't get the sticker he wanted, but he also didn't get sick. Not even a runny nose. My Clorox disinfectant wipes remained intact, despite losing some of my sanity at that moment. My worst fear didn't come true.

This moment is something I come back to when I notice my mind worrying about what could be, what might happen, or what might have happened but didn't. It reminds me that, despite our best efforts, sometimes things just happen, and despite our thoughts that we've ruined something forever, nothing has been ruined. We've never had full control of our lives and we never will. Gulp.

That truth is about as hard to swallow as one of those horse-pill-size vitamin capsules. We're brainwashed to believe that if we just follow this plan, try a little harder, find more willpower, pray more, visualize more, make a vision board, or drink more green juice, we'll be able to rise above all the sadness, the loneliness, the despair, the tragedies, the heartache, the illnesses, and the setbacks, and the flood-gates of goodness will stay open until we live to 100.

Guess what? There's no fool-proof plan. As my friend Alexandra Franzen says, "There's no guarantee for tomorrow, and today is a gift." If you're human, you're going to experience sadness and happiness, pain and pleasure, despair and joy, hopelessness and hope regardless of your size, age, gender, color, or ability. When we begin to accept that all we can do is live life according to life's terms, we can let go of some of the panic, anxiety, and despair haunting us about not only our lives, but about food and body issues in particular. We realize that food can't hurt or heal us. We begin to understand that our body is simply a vessel to participate in this life. The size of that vessel has been largely determined by genetics, and strenuous exercise and food restriction are likely not going to result in lasting change outside of lasting physical and mental harm that we'll likely endure along the way. That vessel probably doesn't look like Kim Kardashian, and even her vessel wouldn't exist without the deft hands of one or more plastic surgeons.

Is it hard for you to imagine giving up on the idea of being able to control your body size or what goes into your mouth? I'm with you. When I first heard this, I thought, "I'm not like Koko the gorilla. I can tell myself what to do and have evolved beyond ape language and thinking." But have I really, I wondered? Am I more animal than human in some ways?

The answer is a surprising yes. We are mammals with some very animalistic behaviors. Tell me that you haven't met humans who display animal characteristics like "pecking order," mercilessness, greediness, competition, and a persistent fight for survival. Tell me you haven't felt those primal urges for food and intimate connection. Tell me you haven't eaten something and thought, "I have no idea why I did that." Sometimes we don't have reasons why, and it's because we're responding to deep biological urges, desires, and needs that are well beyond our rational thinking brain.

You can't think your way thin. You can't "trick" your body out of its biological need for certain types and amounts of foods. Your body is much smarter than any diet culture critic telling you to put your fork down and start backpedaling slowly like you've just been caught shoplifting at the 7-11. You can simply continue to peel back the layers of diet culture so you're free to live your life according to life's terms, not fighting against life's terms to try to achieve the impossible.

I'll never be six-foot-two. I'll never have a size seven shoe. I'll never have blue eyes. I've started to view my body size in this same way, too. I'll never be a size zero. Yes, I still eat fruit and vegetables and move my body in ways that feel good, but I don't do either of these things under the guise that I'll lose weight or live to 100, although a girl can still dream about being a centenarian. Practicing habits with a weight-neutral mindset will help you shed diet culture's thick cloak, so you can feel a little less like you're sporting an x-ray vest and a little more like you're wearing a Superwoman cape.

*For more ideas on letting go of control, I highly recommend author and podcaster Kate Bowler's work and author Pema Chodron's *When Things Fall Apart.*

* * *

SUMMARY

One of diet culture's and western society's biggest myths is that if we just tried a little harder, prayed a little bit more, found more willpower, or drank more green juice, we'd be able to really succeed and avoid pain and suffering. Unfortunately, young people die, vegans get cancer, and priests have heart attacks. The best thing we can do is give up on the false sense of control that we have over our food and bodies and practice living life on life's terms. Our mind is powerful, but not powerful enough to override our genetic wiring for body size. If you weren't constantly trying to control your body size, what would you spend your time, energy, and attention on today, tomorrow, and in the future?

* * *

MANTRA

- I can learn to live life on life's terms.
- I don't have control over everything that happens in my life, and that's okay.
- I don't have complete control over what I eat and can relax knowing my body knows what it needs.

Practice Body Acceptance

My son looked at me sheepishly and started giggling.

"What's so funny?" I huffed after finishing a 30-second plank.

"Umm, Mom, your stomach looks kinda weird."

I looked down at my bare belly between my shorts and sports bra and had a brief but important pause. This pause reminded me that these are the moments where I can teach my kids (and myself) acceptance or disgust. Love or hate. Compassion or criticism.

There was a time when I used to hate many parts of my body and would've likely heard that comment and recommitted myself to a new lifestyle change, including extra cardio, restricted calories, and food elimination. I can honestly say I've drastically eliminated my body dissatisfaction over time, so I was able to look at my son and actually laugh with him.

"It does look kinda funny...sort of like a big marshmallow with a mouth in the middle! But you know what? I love my belly because it was the home for you and your siblings. You all grew inside there, making it a very special place. You started in there as just a tiny seed."

My body is my home, and it's the best part of my body story. Birthmarks, moles, wrinkles, and scars all tell a bit of my story, but none come close to my belly. That sacred space has held life (and non-viable life), hopes, dreams, faith, fear, courage, triumph, tragedy, joy, excitement, and most of all, love.

I think you and I both probably spent way too much time poking, pinching, lifting, grabbing, and pressing in front of mirrors. While these body checking habits can be hard to break, it's important to recognize that using the mirror as a barometer of worth and acceptance is dicey, at best.

In these moments of awareness, try choosing love for yourself, and if that doesn't feel possible, choose acceptance. If acceptance doesn't even feel right, try thinking about your body neutrally by saying to yourself, "I have a body. I have thighs. I have a stomach." Even when it feels hard. Even when it doesn't feel like an option. Because learning to accept your body today is going to be your best chance to accept your body in the future when inevitable changes happen as you age.

Practicing respect for your body will help your kid learn to respect their body, too. If you notice your kid commenting negatively on their body, ask them questions about what they mean. Invite them to consider who makes the beauty rules or standards. Remind them how their body is capable of so much, regardless of their size.

Let's teach our kids to accept all their beautiful parts and to be able to see beauty in many different shapes and sizes. Because trying to chase the impossible air-brushed model ideal is like running on a hamster wheel in shark-filled water. There's danger lurking all around, and it's a no-win situation. If you or your child catch yourself in the dreadful game of compare and despair, follow these steps:

1. Recognize that you're in comparison mode.

2. Check in to see what thoughts you're believing or what your inner critic is telling you.
3. Ask yourself what this voice might be trying to protect you from.
4. Give yourself compassion just as you would offer the same compassion to your kid.
5. Bring yourself back into the present moment, feeling your feet on the ground, and look around to notice a few things you see, hear, taste, or smell. Get your five senses involved to help bring you back home into your body.
6. Imagine your child or best friend was struggling with this same issue. What advice would you give your friend? Write it out and read it back to yourself.

Finally, take some time to ask yourself these important questions: *What could I gain by accepting my body? How would my life change if I focused on acceptance, kindness, and compassion towards myself?*

A resource I like to recommend for teens and tweens is Sonya Renee Taylor's *Celebrate Your Body*. While you're at it, read her other book, *The Body Is Not An Apology*, too.

Another place where practicing body acceptance is important is with photographs. Pictures are hard because they capture a split second in time, and you can look completely different depending on the angle or range the picture was taken. I challenge you to quiet your inner critic enough to get back into pictures and to commit to focusing on what you see outside of your body. Where were you? Who were you with? What happy moment was captured? Can you decide ahead of time to like how you look no matter what? If you need a little photo confidence, I highly recommend the work of Vivienne McMaster (https://www.viviennemcmasterphotography.com) or Lindley Ashline (https://bodyliberationphotos.com/).

* * *

SUMMARY

Whenever you talk about your body (to yourself or in front of your kids), choose the path of acceptance. Think about how it feels for you to practice kindness towards yourself. Think about how it will feel for your child to hear you talking about your body in a respectful and not shameful way. Even if your kindness towards your thighs or stomach feels strange because you've never allowed yourself acceptance, keep practicing. Any new skill feels awkward at first and takes practice. And lastly, talk to yourself the way you would talk to your child or in the way that you would want your child to talk to themselves. What advice would you give a friend who might be struggling with your same issues? Write it down and read it back to yourself.

* * *

MANTRA

- My body is my only home, and I will treat it with respect.
- My body is a miracle, and miracles come in all shapes and sizes.
- My worth and value are never determined by my size; I'm 100% worthy and lovable.

Time to Go Shopping

I passed through the doorway, a dirt-covered jeep half-sunk into the ground with headlights on my left, a stack of boulders on my right. Up ahead, an elephant tusk emerged from the floor while khaki hats with drawstring ties dotted the horizon. A sense of thrill overcame my body.

My sister, mom, and I were embarking on one of my favorite annual traditions. Not a real safari but a trip to the Banana Republic in the Grand Avenue Mall (circa 1988) in downtown Milwaukee, which felt like a pretty close second. The decor was a vintage yet cool scene from the jungle, and I couldn't wait to comb through the racks and stacks of clothes while the jungle beat music played softly.

Every year my sister and I would pick out school outfits at this destination. Even the dressing rooms made it feel like you were going on an adventure with their banana bunches trimming the doorway and palm leaf curtains. The lights were dim, and it smelled like a mix of coffee beans and fresh wood. I loved lingering in the adventure.

A close second to the tropical forest was shopping for modular fashion knitwear from the 80s at Units. Ooh, the matching sets, the colors, the ability to wear one thing five ways! It was the simple, elastic band ease that appealed to the young and old.

Shopping as a kid was fun because it happened often with your constant changes in height, width, and foot size! As a child, I bet you can remember a time when your clothes barely lasted you a season before the hem, the sleeves, the collar, and the width were all too small, too short, and too constricting to be worn for one more second. Your parents probably didn't argue about your need for new clothing, even if they did complain about just buying you that top, those pants, and two pairs of shoes like yesterday! If something didn't fit, you needed to get something else ASAP.

If your child came to you in desperate need of some new gear, you very likely wouldn't try talking them into wearing that pair of shoes for just another few months or keeping the top that was two sizes too small. Nope, you'd figure out what was in your budget and get some comfortable clothes right away.

Isn't it funny that we don't often think of ourselves with these same standards? For some reason, we're taught to believe we should stop growing in our early 20s and stay the same shape and size for the rest of our lives. Well, nothing could be further from the truth. To be alive means our bodies are constantly changing. Remember learning about your natural weight set point range of 5 to 20 pounds? Remember that hormonal and medication changes can affect your size? We all go through different seasons of shapes and sizes, and, very often, those changes are protective of our health. Women very often gain weight around their midsection in midlife, which is actually protective of their health. So much so that this phenomenon is often referred to as acquiring your built-in life preserver.

Jeans or pants not fitting? Don't save them for some rainy day. Get yourself a pair that fits your current body and doesn't pinch or pull or cause you to suck in more than a mouse shimmying through a crack in your basement wall. I can't emphasize enough how important it is for you and your kids to have clothing that's comfortable.

Top too tight in the shoulders? This doesn't mean it's time to try the next best "plan" or "lifestyle change" or go ballistic on your exercise regime. It also doesn't mean you should get into the balloon sleeves/padded shoulders that have been having a moment again since the 90s, unless, of course, that's your thing!

Next time your body changes shape, remind yourself what you would say to your own kid and what you would do for them. There'd be no shame or blame, just a factual realization that it's time to get clothes that fit their body and feel comfortable because nobody wants to wear pants that look like they're waiting for the next flood.

Bodies are never a problem. While the clothing industry is doing a lot more than they ever have to expand their size offerings, there are still many clothing stores that only accommodate straight body shapes. It can be incredibly frustrating and embarrassing for anyone to find clothes that fit and feel comfortable, but even more challenging if you have a larger body. I have several resources at the end of the book for plus-size clothing and encourage every reader to keep advocating for those in larger bodies to have access to fun, fashionable clothing options, too.

Why not have some fun getting new clothes for yourself? Find a shopping experience that was as fun as Banana Republic or Units back in the day. Buy in person, buy online, find some resale shops, or swap with friends. Shopping doesn't need to be expensive. There are so many amazing second-hand online options, like eBay, Poshmark, ThredUp, and TheRealReal. Local resale shops and Goodwill can have incredible finds for a fraction of the price, and Target boutique is always in style. The more we have clothes that don't bind, pinch, pull, or poke at our bodies, the less time we'll be hung up on those body parts.

***

Summary

Your body is constantly changing within your weight range throughout your life. Just because you're out of puberty doesn't mean you'll stay the same shape you were when you were in your 20s. The truth is your body is going to change just like a child's body changes. When your child comes to you in need of new clothing because they've grown, there's no trying to talk them out of the next size(s) up. You simply get them what they need. It's time to do the same for yourself. Make it fun, make it thrifty, or make it both. Just make sure you get the clothing you need to feel comfortable in your body today.

***

Mantra

- My body deserves to have comfortable clothing.
- My body deserves to have clothing that fits.
- I can find clothing that suits my style and maximizes my comfort.

Make Self-Care a Priority

On a recent flight with our family, my 1-year-old fidgeted with every airplane seat button, shade, and flap she could get her hands on. It's a race to see if I can sanitize our little cubicle before she starts exploring and inevitably sticking her fingers in her mouth. Thank you, pacifier, for giving me a fighting chance!

Within minutes, the kind flight attendant knelt down in the aisle and reminded me about all the rules of having a baby on my lap. There's never a time when I haven't had an attendant remind me to put on my own oxygen mask first. Literally, you must take care of yourself first, then help others. It's easy to forget this basic life lesson, but it's important to remember so you can prioritize self-care.

Self-care isn't just a luxury for those who can afford an afternoon at the spa. Self-care is making sure that you take time to ask yourself what you need and then dedicate the time to getting your needs met, even if that means 2 minutes to close your eyes and breathe deeply. If you aren't meeting your own needs, it's hard to be able to continuously give to your family and friends and work inside and/or outside the home.

Closing your door and putting on a "do not disturb" sign up and letting your kids know you'll be unavailable for the next half hour is completely reasonable. Taking a minute for five full, deep breaths while you're in the aisles of Target with a melting down child works, too. Maybe you want to read a trashy magazine, read a book, journal, do yoga, call a friend, take a shower, or just have time to yourself without having one (or more) people repeatedly calling your name or tugging at your clothes. Maybe you feel like you wouldn't even know what to do with your free time. In that case, make yourself a wish list of things you used to have time for and loved, things you've been wanting to try, or something you'd like to learn, and put yourself on the calendar just like you do for your kids.

It's time to reframe self-care as something that's necessary for you and your family's mental health so that you have time to recharge and feel refreshed. Setting this example for your kids is important. Remember that our kids are like sponges absorbing everything we say and do. We want our kids to know that as they grow older and we're not constantly caring for them, they need to prioritize caring for themselves.

If you feel like you're getting some resistance to the idea of self-care, ask yourself what's one small thing you can do to incorporate some time to refuel. Think about what could get in the way and also what you stand to gain by prioritizing your self-care. Remember to think about emotional, spiritual, and physical aspects of your self-care, and really analyze how much of your day you spend doing things for others versus yourself.

During the pandemic, I started to get more serious about my own self-care. Just like I teach my yoga students, I became a curious observer and noticed the things I felt like I needed for my own self-care. These are just 10 small things that I do (some of the time!). All of these suggestions are meant to help inspire you to find what you need. Be curious to find out what would feel good on a daily, weekly, or monthly basis. I encourage you to ask yourself like you'd ask your own child what they need, and then add them to your day to keep you mentally and physically well for the long haul.

1. Get some air. Something about a few minutes outside instantly improves my mood. Whether it's the smell of magnolia trees in spring, snow-covered branches on a winter day, fall leaves changing colors, or summer sun, the vastness of the outdoors and the sounds of life outside bring a sense of renewal. Research shows that spending time outdoors can boost your mood and reduce mental chatter.

2. Move your body. I love to move my body, even if it's a quick walk around the block.

3. Write down five things you're grateful for. I have a journal where I write every night while I'm getting ready for bed. Even during times when not a lot changes each day, it's important to find gratitude for the little (and big) things.

4. Get enough fuel. None of us can function well without sufficient food. As a parent to six kids, I need enough fuel to power me through the day. I don't recommend going more than 3 to 4 hours without a meal or snack during the day. I like to plan some time to make sure I have a handful of things I like, and when I can't get what I want, a C+ meal or snack is fine. Getting adequate energy is what's most important. And my food never looks like the spreads in *SELF* magazine, which are, by and large, diet portions anyways.

5. Smile (or laugh). Okay, that was really two rolled into one, but both are important. Studies show that a genuine smile, the kind where you get crow's feet around your eyes, can actually improve your level of happiness. And we all need

to laugh to get through the inevitable challenging times in our lives.

6. Sleep. This one is tough for many parents, especially those with babies. The recommendation is 7 to 8 hours of solid sleep, and I find that if I don't get that, I don't feel like I have the energy and patience to be a good parent.

7. Five minutes of breathing. I actually set a reminder on my phone for mindful minutes. When I hear the alarm, I remind myself to pause and take a few deep breaths.

8. Weekly yoga. I've been teaching yoga for close to two decades. Having this hour every week to clear my mind, focus on my body, and breath—and help my yogis do the same—is some of my most precious time.

9. Reading for a few minutes at night before bed. This helps me get out of my head and into a great story. For years I just read to our kids at night; now I try to do the same for myself.

10. Talking to or seeing a friend or family member at least once a week. Having connections with other moms and friends is important to my mental health. Picking up the phone instead of sending a text makes a big difference in today's digital world. Prioritizing connections in real life helps fill up my cup. We don't have relatives nearby, so I stock up on that time during our visits over the holidays and the summer.

*A bonus to consider is making plans for things you can look forward to every year. A family trip, a weekend away with your friends, or a solo day trip can all add some fuel to your very important self-burning flame! We make a commitment to have travel plans to look forward to every year as the anticipation of the trip can do as much good for your mental health as the trip itself!

SUMMARY

Self-care isn't just for those who can devote an entire afternoon or day at the spa. Self-care is for all of us and is necessary for your mental and physical health. Take some time to find out what small (or big) things you can add to your daily routine that would help you feel your best. You must always put on your oxygen mask first so that you have the energy both physically and mentally to be able to give to your family and your community.

* * *

MANTRA

- Self-care isn't selfish; it's necessary.
- I'm the most important person to care for in my life.
- Taking care of me helps me care better for everyone around me.
- Finding things that light me up on a daily basis will make me a happier person and mom.

Stop Checking Yourself

I'll never forget the lessons I learned as a little girl in a Marshall Field's dressing room. When I was a kid, it was a huge highlight for my sister and me to go to the fancy department store at the big mall with my mom for school shopping. This seemed even fancier than our trip to Banana Republic or any other mall store because the store had so many departments and everything you'd ever want or need. Combing through the racks of seemingly endless clothes was a close rival to picking out candy in the aisles of our local pharmacy with my best friend.

I'd like to think I picked out classic clothes way back when, but photos of myself in floral Laura Ashley puffed sleeve dresses and rolled jeans clearly show that I was a sucker for trends. It was always a race to get the "cool" things before my sister scooped them up, because the rule was the first person to find an item got to try it and buy it if they liked it.

The picking clothes out part was easy; it was the trying on part of these trips that got a little messy. I'm not sure there are too many people who love the experience of trying on clothes in terrible fluorescent lighting and looking at themselves in weirdly reflecting three-way mirrors. The carpeting in those rooms was always questionable, and the corners were filled with massive dust bunnies and pins from clothing tags or seamstress alterations. Wagering a guess here, but I assume it's a coin toss on whether you'd pick trying on swimsuits in a department store or going to the DMV.

After my sister and I had our loot intact and all those post-shopping adrenaline feels, my mom would try on her items. I felt like I was on pins and needles for what came next. This wasn't our first rodeo, so I would cringe inside knowing what was to come. My mom is a beautiful woman inside and out. She told us that she was much thinner when she was first married at the ripe old age of 22 but that her body had changed over time (no surprise there).

My mom would try something on and inevitably start poking at her stomach or pinching behind her arms or grabbing the skin on her waist and saying how much she wished she could get rid of those parts of her body. "If I could just lose this," she'd say in disgust after picking up a piece of her belly. "I just wish that my stomach was smaller, flatter like you and your sister and like when I was younger."

Now, this was heartbreaking for my sister and me to hear, and we'd rally together like the best two cheerleaders at the high school basketball game to assure her that she looked great and that she didn't need to lose any part of her. Somehow, we'd pull together and walk back out of that dressing room, even if our shoulders were more stooped with the weight of the anti-fat world on our shoulders. I hated that my mom was so sad about how she looked. I wished she could see the beauty I saw in her.

Unfortunately, this wasn't an isolated incident. Mom was a repeat offender of mirror abuse. To this day, she's one of my best friends, so her minor felonies have long been forgiven. She'd check herself at home and give a single word of "ugh" or "yuck" or "what is going on with my hair today?" to express her shame and disgust at what she saw. You see, it's in these small moments in time, in front of bathroom mirrors, dressing rooms mirrors, and storefront reflections, you learn what's considered okay and not okay about your body size. My mom never body shamed my sister and I, but seeing her so upset made my sister and I hyper aware of the sadness that awaited us if we had a body that looked like hers.

What was it like in your home? Did your mom constantly criticize her appearance? Did she pick, poke, squeeze, or suck her way through her days? Was there an environment of full acceptance of size? Was there a need to constantly be "done up" in order to leave the house?

For many years, I found myself being extremely critical about my size, and I think the lessons I learned from my mom gave that inner critic some of the fuel she needed for her decades-long body obsession. I want to be clear that my disordered issues aren't my mom's fault in any way. While her attitude towards her body didn't help, it wasn't the cause of my problems.

I used to check or palpate certain bones to know that I was an "okay" size, grab at the skin to make sure I couldn't pinch more than an "acceptable" amount, and not see any bat wings when waving in the mirror. This practice isn't uncommon with disordered eaters or those with body dysmorphia and is known as body checking.

Letting go of body checking as a practice is a great way to heal your own body image and also demonstrate to your kid that overly obsessing about your body isn't something you value. Not commenting negatively about yourself in the mirror or in the dressing room can be incredibly challenging, but think about how you might be able to soften and allow a little more self-acceptance or even self-love by taking the high road. Remind yourself that you won't actively participate in your own oppression because of some arbitrary standard you've created that's rooted in discrimination.

I invite you to avoid pinching, poking, and grabbing for the next week. What if you decided ahead of time that every time you looked at yourself in the mirror, you'd choose a compliment instead of criticism. If you have the urge to body check, stop and ask yourself what else might be going on in your life that's prompting you to check yourself. It's very likely that you're feeling anxious, worried, or out of control in another area of your life, and body checking is your way to bring about some sense of calm or relief, albeit a false sense of calm.

I encourage you to stop treating your body like it's a problem to solve. What would it feel like to wake up and not look at yourself or have your child view themself as a constant project in the making? Would you rather spend your time on a project that can make your world or someone else's world a little bit better?

You have my permission to skip the mirror entirely for a while or put up a fun note on any mirror in your house that gives you one of the Stuart Smalley-type affirmations, like "I'm good enough" or "I'm a worthy human being" or "All bodies are good bodies" or a simple thumbs up, smiley face, or heart sticker. I know it sounds as cheesy as my dad's dinner jokes, but any little reminder to promote joy over pain is worthwhile.

One final note to consider is to think about other things you can do to reduce any stress or anxiety you might be feeling in any area of your life. Finding ways to handle daily life stressors and accept the body you have today can greatly decrease your desire for body checking.

* * *

Summary

Having the urge to poke, pinch, grab, or palpate bones on your body is very common for dieters and those with high body dissatisfaction. Avoiding this behavior for yourself and your kids is a critical step on your journey to body acceptance. Very often, the desire to body check is prompted by increased anxiety, stress, or worry in other areas of your life. Practicing deep breaths and addressing your needs outside of dieting are two great ways to help reduce this behavior. What would it be like for you to wake up tomorrow and not feel like your body was a fourth-grade science project in need of constant rebuilding and that you weren't a problem to be fixed? How can you develop a more positive attitude when looking at yourself in the mirror? If you've been avoiding your reflection in the mirror and want to be able to see the beauty that every one of us possesses, I encourage you to spend some time getting to know yourself again.

MANTRA

- I don't need to body-check to feel good about my body.
- When I have the urge to body check, I can ask myself what else might be going on?
- My worth, value, and lovability are independent of my size.
- I can look in the mirror and choose a compliment instead of criticism.

Section 8

Managing Feelings and Mindset

Self-Love Isn't Necessary

I watched a lot of game shows as a kid. Kids of the 80s and 90s had *Jeopardy*, *Wheel of Fortune*, and *The Price is Right* to entertain them instead of iPads. If you were lucky enough to grow up in the Midwest, you even had *The Bozo Show* with the grand prize game to get you through your Saturdays. I wanted to be on that show to get the ball in that last bucket and win the 10-speed Schwinn bike so badly!

These days it's the diet industry that's busy distracting us with games. Like that carnival favorite Whack-A-Mole, the dieter stands ready with a thick club to eagerly whack whatever the diet industry is teasing today: a new diet, a new plan, a new cleanse, a new detox. *Over here! No, look at my juice fast over here! No, take my supplement! Quick, over here, try this fasting plan! Back over here to stop eating carbs! Over there again to add in all the fat!* You can never get the moles to all stay down because a shiny new diet is always popping up and promising the next best thing, and NONE of them work long term. It's all a futile attempt to lose weight permanently. The moles, aka "solutions," keep popping up because there's no one proven method that works.

But perhaps the biggest game the diet industry plays these days is the game of love—self-love, that is. Here are the two biggest lies when it comes to weight and love:

1. By loving yourself through dieting, you'll be able to succeed in *this* diet plan.
2. You won't truly love yourself until you're at a smaller size.

Let's talk about the first one. A fellow life coach just sent out an email advertisement with this message: "We will be learning how to embrace and love our bodies. To eat in a way that fuels our bodies because we love them. To reward our bodies for all the hard work they do with the kind of care our bodies crave."

Oh, that's a good one. Did you see what she did there? She wrapped her diet program promising weight loss—rooted in anything but self-care—into a sandwich with self-love spread on the low-carb bread and some fake love sprinkled on the veggies. We indeed want to fuel our bodies and treat them with care for all their hard work, but you can't do that through dieting.

Don't be fooled. Dieting doesn't teach you to embrace and love your body. Dieting dissociates you from your body by teaching you to ignore your own hunger and desire. Imagine that! You have to turn against yourself to make someone else's pocketbook heavy, which will very likely leave you feeling less than. Restriction, on any level, is dangerous both mentally and physically, and it's sad that millions of people are voluntarily doing this to themselves because they don't know the truth.

Diet gurus are sneaky, though. They want you to believe you're going to be loving and caring for your body by forcing it into a smaller size. Because everyone knows that smaller is better, right? WRONG. You already know what you crave (even if diet culture has taught you to silence these cravings), and you know that caring for and LOVING your body looks NOTHING like a diet. Your body doesn't crave deprivation and starvation on any level.

Now let's look at the second love lie. Here's breaking news: You don't even have to love yourself at all. Yep, I said it. It would be unrealistic to believe that everyone loved all their parts. Is it a worthy goal? Yes. Do you have to feel 100% love, 100% of the time, for 100% of your body? No. You can find happiness by simply accepting and respecting the body you have today and practicing self-compassion.

You aren't broken, you aren't a daily project, and you aren't a problem to be fixed. As Sonya Renee Taylor teaches, *the body is not an apology.* And unless we can make peace with our bodies and address our fear of being a certain size, we will stay in the endless loop of the diet cycle, a loop that inevitably includes restriction, which leads to reactionary eating, which leads to you feeling shame and inadequacy, which lands you right back at day one of a different diet. You'll stay stuck in this loop over and over again until you accept your body and lose hope that there's a magical diet that can permanently change your body. Dieting only gets harder as time goes on, but giving up dieting actually gets easier over time.

The list of things we want to change about our bodies is very likely endless. It's okay to acknowledge that you don't like your kid's messy room (*raises hand*). Would you like them to change their ways? Sure. Can you control them? No. You might say something like, "It just is what it is," and that's precisely the same attitude you can adopt for your body. I might not like what I see, but I can't control it, and it is what it is. Think about your body size as part of your physical characteristics, like eye color and height. You don't try to argue with these body "facts," so try expanding your body fact library to open up acceptance about your size, too.

You get to decide your definition of beauty. You get to decide how you show up in the world. You get to have the power to feel good about yourself no matter what. Too often, you're left waiting for approval. Guess what? I've waved my magic wand, and approval has been granted.

Until we realize our happiness, love, acceptance, and power are things we can give to ourselves at any time without anyone else's permission, we're going to keep seeking and striving for an impossible ideal size that's been largely (and falsely) constructed by diet culture. You'll never be "enough." You'll never find your actual power and peace if you're constantly looking outside yourself. You have to find your power and validation from within. Nobody else can or will ever give you what you're looking for.

What if you started believing a different story about yourself? The one that starts with, once upon a time, they learned to accept their perfectly imperfect body and life because they realized they only had one precious chance. How do you want to treat your body? How can you find more ways to respect your body? How can you talk to your kid about respecting their body? Remind them that respect looks like good hygiene, sleeping enough, connecting with friends, moving their bodies in ways that feel fun, getting fresh air, and making sure they're well-fed throughout the day.

You never know when your warranty on life is going to expire, so you may as well enjoy your life by finding sanity around your body and food and accepting the most amazing gift you'll ever receive: yourself. Just imagine Bob Barker calling you to "come on down!" to be the next contestant in the game of your life on *The Price Is Right*.

* * *

Summary

The diet industry has fooled us into thinking that dieting is an act of love. Nothing could be further than the truth. Dieting in itself involves dissociating with and ignoring your body's natural cues and clues about hunger, desires, and satiety. The real act of love is being willing to step away from diet culture and learning to accept and respect the body you have today. You don't need to love your body, but you do need to offer respect for the incredible gift that you've been given. You can love yourself, too; just know that it's not a prerequisite in order to find happiness or peace.

* * *

Mantra

- I can commit to respecting the body I have today.
- I don't have to love every part of myself, but accepting all parts is key.
- Taking care of myself in a weight-neutral way is a form of self-love.
- Dieting is not self-love, and I respect myself too much to participate in dieting anymore.

Release Control to Allow Space

Measuring cups and measuring spoons. Those were my methods of control. For years, my red plastic measuring spoon got more play than any other kitchen "tool" I owned. Nothing on the shiny shelves at Williams Sonoma could hold a candle to that double-sided magic measurer. If I stayed within the recommended serving sizes as supported, promoted, endorsed, and suggested by the Dietetic Association, the diet industry, and the American Food Guide Pyramid, I was "safe," "good," and "in control."

Little did I know that using measuring devices would eventually lead me to feel more out of control with food. Using any outside tool, which inadvertently disconnects you from your body, to indicate how much you should consume will inevitably lead to restriction followed by binge eating. So much for staying within the "guidelines."

But I'd never think to blame my beloved measuring spoons as the problem. No, they were helping me stay "in line" and "on track," and I just needed to use them more. You can see the slippery slope I was climbing with the repeated control, restrict, and binge cycle. I was feeling like a wet puppy that could scurry halfway up a metal slide but come back to the beginning in one fell swoop.

If you've dieted for any period of time, you know that tracking food becomes another full-time job; obsessing about what you eat might feel satisfying yet not take you over your points limit consumes your every waking minute. Dragging your body through intense workouts to offset any of your daily miscalculations becomes the norm. Needless to say, it's a lot physically and emotionally. Trying to control your body size isn't for the faint of heart. The diet gurus like to tell you that you need more grit, strength, or willpower, but I would argue that dieters are some of the toughest people I know. To be able to withstand repeated restriction and surmount physical and mental strain isn't for the faint of heart.

Have you ever stopped to wonder what would happen if you took the focus off how many Peloton rides you did or kombuchas you drank per week? Have you ever wondered what you might be thinking about or dealing with if you weren't constantly obsessing about food and your body? Have you ever stopped to think that dieting itself might be the habit you need to quit because it's serving as your way to manage anxiety, stress, or your lack of control in the world? Have you ever thought that dieting itself was the real addiction?

Diet culture will have you believe you should be able to control your body shape and size through diet and exercise. The old 1980s belief that inside every fat person, there's a skinny person waiting to get out is completely false. I hope by now I've convinced you that while permanently manipulating your body is an appealing idea, it just doesn't work in real life. Our size is largely determined by genetics, our environment, stress levels, and many other biological factors.

As a dieter, you very likely turned to dieting time and again as a way to gain control of your body, yes, but also your life. Insert the mind-blown emoji here because that's sometimes a hard truth to swallow. Yes, there's messaging we've internalized around food and our bodies and dieting, yet you've likely never been told that dieting is often used as a tool to soothe anxiety.

Eating disorders are very often linked with anxiety. If you've experienced anxiety, you know it's not comfortable. Instead of dealing with your anxiety head on, you naturally look to outside measures to soothe your racing mind and jittery body. As humans, we're programmed to seek pleasure and avoid pain. Calorie counting, food rules, and measuring foods are all tactics and practices in control, yet the irony of it all is that the more you restrict and control, the more out of control you feel around food. Your body can only handle deprivation for so long before it sends you into a binge/reactionary eating episode. Some of you have been using dieting as a great distraction from what's actually going on in your life or as a way to cope with the anxiety you never knew was there because you thought having anxiety meant you needed to be curled up in the fetal position breathing into a paper bag. Anxiety looks different for everyone who experiences it and can show up in subtle and not-so-subtle ways.

To stop using dieting as a coping mechanism is a process, to say the least. The first step with much of this work is simply awareness. Imagine these scenarios. Your kid gets sent to the principal's office for getting in a fight, so you skip breakfast and lunch because you spend most of the day in worry mode. Your kid never listens to you and is starting to spit at their siblings. You've tried every parenting trick, but nothing is working. So you start researching a new "lifestyle" plan because at least someone can make a change in your house. Interesting.

It's very subtle to notice this addiction of sorts because dieting is condoned, encouraged, promoted, and celebrated. Once you're onto yourself, I recommend the next time you reach for a measuring cup or turn the package to view calorie labels, pause and ask yourself, *"If I wasn't trying to control my body with food restriction, what would I be thinking about? What might be bothering me? What uncomfortable feelings might I be feeling? What would avoiding these thoughts or feelings do for me? In what way is my body trying to protect me from potential pain?"*

In yoga I teach my students to become a curious observer during class. When you take on the position of the curious observer, you don't use judgment and are better able to explore possibilities on and off your mat. Without judgment, you can begin to develop tools to process your emotions. You can put the measuring cup down, take a few minutes for yourself (which could start with five deep breaths), and then explore what's there for you. Instead of turning away from difficulty, practice turning toward it.

Interestingly, those with a history of dieting tend to turn to food as a coping mechanism, whereas those without a history of dieting find other coping strategies. Remember, it's never wrong for you or your child to soothe difficult emotions with food. Emotional eating—that is, eating to soothe difficult feelings or emotions—is a perfectly okay and acceptable coping strategy. Remember that emotional eating can very often turn into binge eating if you are shaming, blaming, or beating yourself up for any reason. Allowance of emotional eating is key to letting go of the perceived grip that food has over you. I simply invite you to get curious when you notice that you're hungry but you tell yourself no, when you want to enjoy cake but decline the offer, or when you start googling diet programs.

Some final questions to ponder: If it wasn't an option to deny yourself because you lived on a planet where nobody cared about your size, what would you be thinking about? What ways outside of dieting could you use to calm your nervous system that wouldn't cause lasting physical and mental damage?

SUMMARY

Dieting is so widely accepted in our culture that it seems strange to think that dieting itself may be the thing you're addicted to instead of food. Using dieting as a way to manage and reduce anxiety is very common, although not a strategy that promotes long-term success. You can never address your feelings if every time difficulty arises, you're off counting your almonds and not counting the things you can do to actually manage life's inevitable difficulties. The next time you reach for a recipe to use your ground flax seeds or wonder if your bulletproof coffee can last you until 3 p.m., stop and get curious about what's happening in your life, what really needs attention, and how you can find other ways to calm your nervous system outside of diet culture's empty promises. Remember, diet practices eventually leave you feeling more out of control than ever.

* * *

MANTRA

- If I wasn't dieting, what would I be thinking about?
- If I wasn't trying to control my body size, what might I be focused on instead?
- Using dieting as a tool to soothe my anxiety or difficult feelings isn't a long-term strategy for success.
- I can stop dieting and handle what feelings arise.

Tame and Name Your Inner Critic

Starting a new school is never easy.

Getting verbally threatened the first few days at your new school makes it even harder.

I'll never forget when my daughter came home and told me that a girl said she was going to kill her. Just a joke? Maybe. Being new to the school, she didn't know this girl. New or school veteran, this wasn't acceptable. I called the school the next day to get things sorted. All ended up fine, but it got me thinking.

Would you ever sit back quietly and watch your child get bullied on the playground?

If another kid was screaming derogatory insults at your child (*"You're lazy, ugly, worthless, disgusting, you'll never succeed!"*) throwing things at their face, scratching them, hitting them, putting them in physical or emotional danger, would you sit back, sip your latte, and do nothing?

I'll assume you answered no.

You wouldn't just sit there passively. No way! If your child's safety is being threatened, your mama bear (or papa bear) instincts fire up and you intervene—right away.

But what about the bully who lives inside your own mind?

When that bully starts hurling insults at you—do you intervene? Or do you sit back and take the abuse?

If you have a history of dieting, restricting your food, or orthorexic behaviors (which means an excessive preoccupation with eating healthy foods), it's very likely that you have a cruel bully in your mind. It's like an abusive relationship—with yourself. Worse still, you condone this relationship by sometimes (or very often) agreeing with what this bully has to say.

This bully is very likely feeding on your shame and guilt. Both of these are powerful emotions and are the *currency of diet culture.* When you feel guilty, you believe you did something wrong, and when you feel shame, you believe you are wrong or inherently bad. Without these feelings, we'd have a much easier time flipping the middle finger to our inner critic and diet culture, but because of our years of internalizing diet culture's messaging, to no fault of our own, we pause and listen and agree because this voice is reinforcing a negative thought loop we already believe about ourself.

"Yes, I shouldn't have eaten that. I feel so guilty." Hello, guilt.

"I can't believe I failed again; there must be something wrong with me!" Hello, shame.

Hello, fuel for diet culture's raging inferno.

You and I literally have thousands of thoughts a day, so it would be impossible to completely eliminate these thoughts. It's also good to practice accepting all parts of your body, including your thoughts. Saying that you believe there's not one person out there who doesn't wish to change something physically or otherwise about themselves would be like saying Beyoncé and Mariah Carey aren't good singers. How can you put an end to this abusive relationship? One of the first steps is to notice when your inner bully chatter starts getting louder and recognize that this bully's voice is not "the truth." Hearing a voice, recognizing it, and not giving it any attention or time on your playlist is the strategy.

ED, or an eating disorder, is the acronym writer Jenni Schaefer (jennischaefer.com) coined as a way to create some distance in her mind from her eating disordered thoughts. ED is the name she gave to her inner bully, which she describes in her book, *Life Without Ed.*

Whenever ED would start chattering about Jenni's weight or size or ability to control herself, she would remind herself that "This is just ED talking. It's not the truth, and it's not the real me."

ED was persuasive and persistent, and she had to work hard to realize that SHE was not ED.

ED tried to make her believe she was only virtuous when she listened to him. But ED was not her true voice. ED was the years and layers of cultural brainwashing about her size, her worth, and her health.

Give your inner bully a name, as Jenni did. It might be ED. Or it might be something else—Obsessive Olivia, Nit-Picky Nancy, the Troll, the Gremlin, or another name you choose. Name this voice like you're naming a monster in a children's storybook—a beastly, vicious creature that is currently living inside your brain. This creature is NOT your friend. And this creature is not YOU. It's an unwanted visitor in your head. An intruder.

Then, when you hear this voice arising in your mind, intervene—just like you would intervene if you saw a bully harassing your child at the park. Do something right away—text a friend, call your therapist, email your coach, breathe deeply, chat with yourself, give yourself a hug, do a yoga pose, or anything else that will calm your nervous system down, do whatever you need to do at that moment—to silence that bullying voice. Can you replace your inner critic with your inner coach, who might say something like, "(Use your first name), you can do this." "You're okay." "You're safe." In time, you can learn how to replace this bullying voice with a voice of love and caring—just like I've done, and just like Jenni did, too.

Check in with compassion with your body. Take care of yourself just like you would take care of your child.

"What do you need right now, sweetheart?"

That's the only question I want you to ask yourself today. When you answer this question, consider what advice you might give a friend in your same situation, too.

This is a gentle, loving question that steers you in the right direction—further and further away from ED until eventually, his voice is just a faint cry way off in the distance, not the loudest voice in your mind.

Think about what you need today…and be brave enough to give it to yourself.

* * *

SUMMARY

Everyone has a voice inside of them that's about as nice as an internet troll trying to bring down their archenemy. Believe it or not, your inner critic is very likely trying to help or protect you, but they're going about it the wrong way. When you notice this voice, the first thing to do is simply have the awareness that your inner meanie is talking. Be able to separate this voice from you because they aren't one and the same. To help with this separation, I highly recommend you give this voice a name so you can quickly recognize this voice isn't you. Knowing you don't have to agree with or listen to this voice is an important step in feeling more at peace with your body and food. Instead of getting caught up in the story your voice is trying to sweep you into like a daytime soap opera, ask yourself what you need at this moment. Ask yourself how you can find ways to feel supported, connect with a friend, family member, coach, or therapist, and explore ways to calm your nervous system. Give yourself the same advice you'd give a friend, and direct your brain and thinking in a new direction.

* * *

MANTRA

- Recognizing my inner critic is the first important step.
- Asking what my inner critic might be trying to protect me from can be helpful.
- Finding ways to feel compassion toward myself, like I would toward my child or friend, is crucial.

Become a Feelings Locator

Ninety seconds.

It's less than the time you need to microwave leftovers. It's definitely less time than you spend waiting for your potty-training toddler to do his or her business. And it's absolutely less time than it takes to figure out where you left your phone (ahem, soccer field 4B last Saturday).

Ninety seconds also happens to be the lifespan of a feeling—like anger, fear, or shame. Just 90 seconds. This has been confirmed by neuroanatomists who study how humans respond to stressful situations.

Here's how it works:

First, a stressful event happens. For instance, you get a critical email from a colleague. You see a photo of your ex (with their new partner) on Instagram. Or you realize you're overdue on a bill. Yikes.

Your body reacts to this event with an intense rush of emotion. It might be... Anger. Fear. Shame. Guilt. Anxiety. Loneliness. Disgust. This emotional rush will usually rise, peak, and then decline in the span of 90 seconds. (I know. It feels like it's going to last forever. But it doesn't.)

If you breathe slowly and just "ride it out" for 90 seconds, the intensity of the emotion subsides pretty quickly. After 90 seconds, you might not feel "completely amazing," but you will feel significantly better. Ninety seconds is all it takes for the feeling to flow through you.

The problem is that most people can't stand waiting for 90 seconds. Because when you're experiencing an uncomfortable emotion, like shame, 90 seconds feels like *an eternity.*

And so, as soon as that first wave of shame rushes through your body, what happens? After 2 or 3seconds, *ugggh,* you just want to *do something.* Literally anything to escape this uncomfortable feeling.

And then what happens? Probably you reach for something to numb out and escape. You reach for your phone to distract yourself. Reach for the remote and look for your next HBO obsession. Or you react impulsively—firing off a snarky email you later regret. Whoops.

And thennn what happens? By numbing out or acting impulsively, you make the situation even worse. You feel even crummier than before. You wind up *prolonging* the unpleasant emotion—longer than it needs to be!

But what if you can ride out that emotion?

If you can ride it out for 90 seconds—feeling the discomfort, being with it, and letting it move through you—this changes everything. You'll feel much more "in charge" of your emotional state. And it becomes easier to make choices that nourish you rather than ones that deplete you.

So the next time you feel an intense emotion surging through your body, try this:

1. Become aware of your feeling and name the feeling. *"This is fear." "This is an embarrassment." "This is happiness."*

2. Notice the physical sensations that arise in your body. Flushed cheeks. Heart pounding. Heavy chest. Tight throat. Bonus points if you can describe the feeling in further detail—what is the color, shape, and size of this feeling? Is it moving or still, fast or slow, smooth or rough?

3. Breathe into the physical sensations. Don't resist what is happening. Just let it happen. Remember: It's a short ride. Just 90 seconds.

4. Stay with the feeling for the full 90 seconds. Watch the clock if it's helpful. Watch the changes that arise in your body from a curious scientist's point of view. You can even place your hands over the spot where you feel your emotion as if you're comforting a child. No need to try lessening the feeling or changing it—simply stay with it and offer compassion.

5. Remind yourself that there is nothing to fear: *"This is just an emotion. This is just a vibration in my body. I'm safe. This is temporary. This will pass."* When you notice the feeling pass or begin to shift, take another big, deep breath. Ahhhh. You made it to the other side.

Notice.
Breathe.
Let it flow through you.

When you learn how to feel your feelings and are *willing* to feel your feelings, you realize that you can handle anything. Suddenly, things don't seem so scary anymore.

Teaching your child to sit with and move toward discomfort is one of the best skills you can teach, and you can even practice this together. In yoga, I like to teach my clients to twist toward and not away from what they're bringing to their mat. Feelings aren't fluff. Feelings (good and bad) are the ticket to finding true happiness.

Next time you experience some big feelings, remember that they will pass. You can handle anything for 90 seconds. Really, you can.

* * *

SUMMARY

Our culture tends to be very good at shoving feelings under the rug like a toddler who's too busy to put their toys where they actually belong. Feelings? What are those, and what do I do with them? It's very common for all of us to want to avoid feeling our feelings. I would say that dieters especially have a knack for avoiding difficult feelings by using dieting as a distraction. The next time you have a feeling (good or bad), I encourage you to just have the awareness and name the feeling. Notice where that feeling is in your body, breathe into the physical sensations, and stay there for 90 seconds (or more), and remember there's nothing to fear. This too shall pass.

* * *

MANTRA

- Being able to feel my feelings is one of the most important skills to learn.
- When I have an intense feeling, I can go toward it instead of away from it.
- The worst that can happen is a feeling, a vibration in the body, and I can handle any feeling.
- No feeling (good or bad) lasts forever.

Learn the Truth About Emotional Eating

In my binge eating days, I would try finding out what was wrong with me and why I was eating larger amounts of food at night. I kept coming back to the question, am I an emotional eater? Was it wrong to eat more than what was pictured in *Health* magazine or the USDA nutrition chart? Was this my label? Was this my problem? Was there some deep, dark secret I needed to expose to solve all of my emotional problems and stop eating so much? I'd think back to my childhood and knew there wasn't a big-T traumatic event. There also wasn't any tragic event that was hard to recover from. I had loving and supportive parents and an incredibly supportive extended family, too. Hmm, what was the root of my problems? Why did I seem to turn to food when I was dealing with difficult emotions?

Have you ever found yourself at the end of a stressful day in front of the TV with your fingers fishing out the last crumbs of what used to be a full chip bag 30 minutes ago? Or maybe you've ended up scraping the bottom of an ice cream pint with your favorite spoon in a matter of minutes after a long day of sibling rivalry, endless house chores, and school homework? Like me, maybe you've thought,

"Ugh, I did it again! I'm such an emotional eater! What's wrong with me?"

There's nothing wrong with you, and there was nothing wrong with me.

Here are three important truths to know about emotional eating:

1. People with a history of dieting are much more likely to eat emotionally than non-dieters. Those with no history of dieting actually tend to turn away from instead of toward food during stressful situations. Dieters have trained their brains to use food as a coping mechanism in terms of using it as something to control.
2. Controlling our food intake through restriction eventually results in eating more food (very likely more than you'd normally eat) in order to make up for lost nutrients. This act of making up for lost nutrients often gets labeled as binge eating, but I like to think of this eating as reactionary eating, which is a term coined by my mentor, Isabel Foxen Duke. If you've ever been on a diet, you've undoubtedly noticed that during the day, you're "so good" around food, but at night you just can't control yourself and end up eating all the things you tried to avoid eating during the day. It's a very common physical reaction that makes sense when you understand the "why" behind your body's actions.

Reactionary eating is your body's natural, yes *natural*, reaction to food deprivation. This type of eating can be magnified when difficult feelings arise because not only is the body physically in need of food, but mentally you feel your stress or any other difficult feeling makes it that much harder to resist food. Think of it as a bow and arrow. You can only keep pulling the bow back so far before it eventually snaps back. You can only keep restricting so long before your body (thankfully!) needs to make up for all of the lost nutrients. It's like a pendulum that's pulled so far in one direction and needs to swing all the way to the other side as a course of its natural movement.

Believe it or not, this is your body's way of saving your life. Your body's reaction to starvation is to eat a lot because it doesn't know when it might have the chance to eat food again. You could be living in a house full of food, but your body is in full starvation mode if you're constantly restricting. This is why this type of eating often feels very primal and uncontrollable. Your body doesn't care how the food gets into your body; it just knows that it needs food NOW. These foods are preferably high in carbohydrates or sugar as these nutrients are easily absorbed and provide energy to the body very quickly.

Eating to soothe difficult emotions or situations is totally okay and normal. Our behaviors around food are never the problem; it's our thoughts about these behaviors that often cause us to feel shame and guilt and lead us to believe that our actions are problematic. Non-dieters eat various amounts of food and don't question whether it is emotional eating or "normal" eating. They simply eat without doubt, fear, or question. Go ahead and polish off that pint of ice cream; just be sure that you're offering yourself or your kid additional tools that can help address any difficult underlying emotions.

If you're alive and human, your life is going to be equal parts happy and sad. It's during the not-so-happy times that we can focus on tools for self-regulation, like meditation, calling a friend, getting outside in nature, yoga, feeling our feelings by simply naming our experience, practicing deep breaths or journaling, dancing, or being in communion with others. We can't (our body has its own insanely intricate plan that's beyond our conscious mind for how much food we need) and don't need to control the food part, but we can control how we face hard situations and feelings by finding additional ways to cope. This doesn't mean put the food down and take a bubble bath.

This does mean eating what your body is calling you to eat AND then finding ways to manage your feelings, whether that means taking a bath or watching a comedy show on TV. Remind yourself that feelings and any behaviors around food are both welcome here.

If you have a diet mentality around emotional eating, like "I shouldn't be doing this," "I'm so wrong," "This (aka my actions and who I am as a person) is so bad," you'll very likely turn your emotional eating into binge eating. What might have started out as one cookie turns into the entire Girl Scout Thin Mint sleeve plus whatever else isn't nailed down in your refrigerator. If you judge your eating behaviors as not okay, boom, you're off to the binge eating races.

The key to recovering from both emotional and binge eating is full allowance around food and no physical OR emotional restriction. Remember that you can't feel out of control around something unless you're trying to control it in the first place.

* * *

SUMMARY

Emotional eating gets a bad rap these days, but this label and type of eating is very misunderstood. It's important to know that this eating behavior is largely seen in those who are currently dieting or have dieted. Eating this way is also very closely linked with those who restrict their food intake on a regular basis. Think of it as a bow and arrow, and know that the bow always snaps back at some point. You can't keep pulling back or restricting without needing the opposite behavior of eating a lot of food to balance out the restriction. It's also important to remind yourself that it's absolutely okay to turn to food during stressful times. Food has the ability to soothe and comfort and help you feel good, and there's nothing wrong with that. Because life is about feeling the full range of emotions and having coping strategies along with the range, be sure to find ways (in addition to food) that you can cope with stressful times, too. It's important to have creature comforts like ice cream and know how to address your underlying feelings, too. I like to compare this to Corduroy, the bear who lost his button. Lisa, his new owner, loves the bear no matter what; she just thinks he might be more comfortable with a new button. Like Corduroy, your lovability is already 100%, and your job is to find ways to feel more comfortable when times get tough.

MANTRA

- What I eat is not the problem; it's how I think about what I eat that's the problem.
- I can enjoy food after a stressful day or non-stressful day without guilt.
- I'm working on making sure I get enough food to eat throughout the day.
- I can take care of my body's desire for food and my mind's need for peace and connection.

Become a Curious Observer

I moved around my yoga class, offering suggestions, adjusting bodies, and exploring what was possible with each of my students. I'm a firm believer that yoga is one of the best ways to begin that crucial dialogue of listening and responding to your body, calming your nervous system, finding your edge, and also becoming a curious observer.

As a yoga teacher for over two decades, I still get excited about the discoveries that will be made while my students are sitting, twisting, breathing, holding, stretching, and challenging themselves in every moment on their mat. No matter how many times you do the same pose, you're doing that pose on a different day, at a different time, and you're bringing a different set of physical and emotional circumstances to the mat.

One of the things we lose through dieting is the connection to our bodies. You may have noticed yourself talking to your body a lot more than you listen to your body as a dieter. As a dieter, you trained yourself to ignore hunger signals along with your needs and desires, and that takes a lot of talking with very little listening. You may have heard your body in your dieting days but told it to be quiet so you didn't have to respond with food or rest or anything else that may have interfered with your dieting success.

In order to repeatedly follow any diet system that restricts your energy requirements, you have to detach from your body. "Stop listening to your excuses!" your diet guru pleads so you can finally succeed. "Just ignore what your body and mind are saying" becomes a phrase you live by because supposedly, the diet plan is all-knowing, and that inner voice is just pesky and couldn't possibly be wise. You are told that not only are you smarter than this voice, but you can and should learn how to outwit it, too. The old 80s slogan of "no pain, no gain" gets repeated as you try sticking to your grueling new movement regime.

Except this repeated ignoring of your body backfires like an old Chevrolet pickup with too little fuel and too much air. You have a stressful conversation with your boss/friend/spouse and think, "Eh, I don't need to feed myself, even though I know I'm hungry." You repeat the same thing day after day until finally, your body has you completely obsessing over food, so you start lunging at anything and everything you can get your hands on. You wonder what's wrong with you. You wonder why you failed, again.

Instead of throwing your hands up in disgust like the football coach who didn't like the referee's call and diving head first into the dieter's deep end, pause and ask yourself a better question.

Instead of the age-old "what's wrong with me?" pretend you've become the assistant scientist to Marie Curie. GET CURIOUS.

Ask yourself:

What's going on here?

What's happening in my life that might be stressful? Oh right, I just had that difficult conversation.

What am I feeling right now? I'm really stressed.

Have I been restricting my food in any way today or for a period of time? Oh right, I have been skipping breakfast every day, which is why I'm eating a lot more at night.

Ahhh, now this is all making sense. I'm feeling stressed and anxious about a difficult fight, and as a way to control the situation, I'm restricting my food intake.

Once you've listened to your body, the next step is to respond. Sometimes it's easy to listen, but to do what our body is actually wanting is hard and sometimes scary. This is totally normal. Start slowly and ask it what it needs. What can you offer to feel better right now?

AS AN OBSERVER, YOUR JOB IS TO STAY NEUTRAL. Your job is to trust your body as the infinitely wise human it is. There's no judgment; there's just compassion.

Once you have your information, ask yourself what you can do to help yourself, just like you would offer care and compassion to your kid who was in the same situation. *Who can I call? Do I need to rest? Am I in need of some connection? Do I need to get something to eat? Do I need more stimulation? Less stimulation?*

Know that you're not alone. There isn't a feeling or situation that someone else hasn't experienced, struggled with, or grappled with. See if you can work on finding your edge, meaning that place where you feel challenged enough but not too challenged. Becoming a curious observer today will help you soften and surrender around yourself and your food. Be sure to include a heavy dose of self-compassion as you go through this process.

SUMMARY

Instead of using our inner voice as a way to beat ourselves up about anything and everything, use that voice as the gateway to connecting with what your body really needs. If you have any experience with dieting, you've very likely become good at ignoring your body's wants and needs. To begin this repair process, simply notice when things start feeling crazy in your life. Take on the role of the curious observer. Become your own detective and find out what you're feeling and what you need. Listen to your wise self, and most importantly, actually respond to what your body is asking for—more food, more rest, less stress, more fun, less screen time, etc. Know that you're not alone in any feeling or situation. Even if you feel you're the only one that's ever had this problem, it's simply not true. Get curious, put your judgments aside, and tend to your body's needs. Only you can possibly know what you need.

* * *

MANTRA

- I am a curious observer of my body.
- I am working on not making judgments about myself.
- I am finding ways to care for myself when I notice I'm feeling stressed.

Section 9

Diet Proofing Your Home

Toss Your Scale

As a kid, I used to love hanging out in the bathroom while my mom was getting ready for work or to go out with my dad. I loved her bathrobe, sweet-smelling lotion, the light pink plastic tub of powder she let me puff onto my body, the smell of hairspray, and the way the bathroom stayed cozy from the lingering warmth of her shower that left steam on the mirrors. It was like our secret little hideaway.

Sometimes my mom would start her routine with a check on the scale. She'd pull the scale out from below the cabinets. I can still picture that window with the springy little lever landing on her "number." She'd describe this ritual as a way to "check" where she was so she didn't get too high and stayed in her "range." It was there that I realized that some numbers were good and some were bad. It was in that secret hideaway that I'd start to do my daily checks, too. Don't get too high, and even better if you can get lower.

I began to rely on this piece of metal and plastic as a gauge of my success or failure. I used it as a way of knowing what I could and couldn't have and as a form of self-punishment if that lever didn't go my way. Looking back, those habits fueled my anxiety and kept me spiraling deeper and deeper into the diet world, like an oil digging machine scraping the depths of the earth.

Being able to finally let go of this piece of arbitrary daily information was a powerful process in my recovery. To this day, I refuse to have a scale (for bodies or food) in our home. Our kids often wonder how much they weigh, and I simply guess every time. I want my kids to know that the numbers don't matter to me unless, of course, their weight goes down, which is cause for concern and a conversation with their doctor.

How did I let the scale go? I simply changed the way I thought about what the scale was actually doing and not doing for me. I realized that it was causing more harm than good, and it was keeping me stuck in that endless dieting loop. It was an arbitrary measure that took on a life of its own because of what I made the number mean.

Think about it this way. Imagine that you have a coach you can check in with daily to get a general read on your feelings and set your mood for the day. The coach isn't even virtual; they're right in your own home; usually, the bathroom is the best spot. You find mornings are the best time to check in when you're feeling rested and optimistic about a fresh start. When you start using this coach, you'll be tempted to use them multiple times a day to get that constant feedback you crave. They simply report back the facts, so it's hard to argue with them.

Except this one fact isn't even close to the big picture, but it can very easily take over your life. This single number from your scale, aka "coach," means nothing, yet it assigns your mood, how you feel, your value, your ability to be happy, your ability to be successful, and how much you need to restrict your food or move your body on any given day.

If you've dieted, the scale has undoubtedly been a constant companion, albeit about as good a friend as a school bully. A bully is someone who habitually seeks to intimidate or harm those whom they perceive as vulnerable. I can't think of a more vulnerable group than women who've been constantly told that they aren't thin enough, pretty enough, cellulite-free enough, or wrinkle-free enough. It's not your fault you feel this way, yet you voluntarily step on a scale that spits out a number, which, let's be honest, can change after a trip to the bathroom or by guzzling a 16 ounce water bottle. This machine is fickle, maybe, but really the human body is fickle. You and I are constantly changing throughout the days, months, and years. Very rarely does that number read out to meet your "hopes and dreams" fantasized number.

These natural fluctuations of about 5 to 20 pounds can be accounted for by the weight set point (WSP) theory. You see, every person has a unique WSP, which you can think about like you would the thermostat in your house. When it gets too cold or too hot, your thermostat kicks in to keep the overall temperature of your house in the right range. Your body works very much the same; there's a weight at which your body functions optimally, and it can fluctuate 5 to 20 pounds in either direction, and you're still in exactly the right place for your body. Your body has to work VERY hard to go above or below this range, which is why repeated food restriction always ends up with more food consumption than you might normally eat because your body is like, "HEY! Who's messing with my heating system? We need to get some extra calories in STAT to warm this place up!"

Knowing that you have this range, it seems like a waste of time to step on a scale daily and let that number dictate your mood, your feelings, or your worth. How would it feel if you gave up your daily weigh-ins? Would you feel a sense of relief? Would you feel compelled to still use the scale as a safety measure? If you truly think you can step on the scale and have a neutral reaction to the number you see, like when you step outside and see the grass is green and the sky is blue, then go for it. Only you can know what's best for you and your mental health.

I will say that scales are one of the most triggering things for dieters, as they're a constant measure of diet culture's determined "failure" or "success." How many times have you read that number and felt a sense of dread and panic overtake your body? How many times have you stepped off that Silver God swearing that you'll double down tomorrow? If you have any inkling that it's time to toss your scale, I highly recommend that you toss it or, better yet, take your scale outside immediately and whack it with a sledgehammer like another coach mentor of mine, Summer Innanen, who I highly recommend as an amazing resource for all things body image and anti-diet related.

If you're not yet convinced to part with your scale, keep asking yourself what the daily, weekly, or monthly weigh-ins are giving you. If it's control you're looking for, remember that having absolute control over any particular area of your life is a fool's errand. Achieving that is about as likely as winning the Powerball lottery tonight. Being able to throw your hands up like you're in the front seat of Thunder Mountain at Walt Disney World is the best, albeit hardest, attitude to adopt around your food and body. My mentor, Isabel Foxen Duke, is constantly reminding her clients that their "food and body are going to be what they're going to be." You don't have to be in control because it's impossible to have full control, which is great news if you're a committed list maker like me. Check, check, and check.

Just like body checking, when you have the urge to have the Silver God "coach" you on your weight, stop and ask yourself what else might be going on. Where else might you be feeling stressed or anxious? Maybe it's time for you to find a new coach that gives you a more positive barometer of the amazing human you are, and maybe you can slowly let go of the number on that dial, expand your definition of worth, and teach your kids that using a machine of any sort is never a good way to determine your mood, your worth, your success, or your happiness. Let's teach our kids that they're more than the number on the scale, just like you teach them that they're more than the number they get on a standardized test.

When you feel like you aren't meeting society's standards and head down a shame spiral, I invite you to take a pause. The way out of shame isn't necessarily to change behavior like getting on the scale or searching for a new protocol or isolating yourself and disconnecting. The goal is to find connections. If you can't find it in another human, give it to yourself by reminding yourself that you're not alone, assuring yourself that there's someone else who's felt this same way or is feeling this same way right now. Fortunately, your struggle isn't unique. You can get curious, so you can understand what feelings are tied with shame and then start to work on building a new framework that will lead to lasting change or, at the very least, allow compassion for being human.

One final note, which is a reminder from an earlier section: I highly encourage you to think about whether being weighed at your doctor's office is triggering for you. You can refuse to be weighed— yes, you really can do this—or you can also ask to be weighed blind, meaning you step on the scale with your back to the numbers. You can explain that you've struggled with body image in the past and that you don't want to know the numbers, or simply ask them not to read the number aloud. You can also ask your pediatrician not to talk about weight at your kid's appointments and to let you know if there are any concerns you'd like to talk privately.

* * *

SUMMARY

Using the scale as a measure of weight, and therefore supposed "health," isn't the habit we want to be reinforcing for ourselves or our kids. A single number can never give us the whole picture or even close to the whole picture of our health. How much of your life have you allowed the number from the scale to determine your worth, your value, your success, or your happiness? How many visits to the scale have left you feeling happy, refreshed, motivated, and inspired? Sure, you may have been "happy" during the initial weight loss as you began a diet, but over time, the scale inevitably changes. Saying goodbye to your scale is a great step in the anti-diet journey, and if you can't quite part ways yet, just step on the scale knowing full well that you aren't in control of your body size like the diet industry wants you to believe. Weight loss works for a tiny, I mean *tiny*, fraction of the population, and showing your kid that they need any outside measure to affirm their worth or value isn't the best idea.

MANTRA

- My worth and value are already 100%.
- I won't rely on a number to decide my mood or my health.
- A scale can't capture the numbers that really matter in my life.

Do a Pantry and Refrigerator Edit

I stood in my kitchen looking at the brown Bragg's bottle wrapped in a cheery yellow label. I had geared myself up in the name of "health" to add this miracle elixir to my arsenal so I would lower my blood sugar, aka stop craving sweets. Bonus that it was an antimicrobial with antioxidant effects! One to two tablespoons of this natural liquid could even aid in weight loss, *not that I really cared about that*, cough, cough. I could either drink a shot glass of this stuff or mix it with a full glass of water. One whiff of the pungent apple cider vinegar made the shot glass look like the lesser of two evils. I tried to get past the smell. Staring the liquid down, I reminded myself that it was full of nutrients! Rids the body of toxins! Aids in digestion! Balances blood sugar and might help my waistline! I'm not sure how many days I lasted on the shot glass of what tasted like straight acid with a woody aftertaste, but let's just say I didn't get close to the halfway mark on that cheery yellow label line.

How many times have you tried to down a wheatgrass shot or kale chips or kombucha tea in the name of "health?" Remember Snack-Wells? Celery juice? How many different "health" bars have you tried that left you feeling like you had chalk or dirt or a combination of the two lingering in your mouth for hours? No. Thank. You. I knew there had to be a better way.

I'm sure you can remember buying into the latest fad promising a brand new you with repeat consumption. The problem with most of these products is that the "health" they're promising is really the promise of weight loss or weight maintenance at a minimum.

I've long given up diet foods but recently had an unfortunate tortilla purchase at our house that brought back all the bad-tasting diet foods. It started with a chorus of complaints during dinner.

"Ewwww, gross!"

"These are disgusting! OMG, I just won't eat anything."

"What's wrong with these, Moooooom???"

"Yuck. Just nasty."

The offender of this particularly terrible meal? Maria and Ricardo's tortillas made from quinoa.** We're obsessed with Maria and Ricardo's regular flour tortillas and devour them on Taco Tuesdays, but these dairy-free, wheat-free, made with avocado oil imposters were bad. Really bad. And I fully admit they were gross and happily tossed the untouched quinoa burrito imposters.

In my dieting days, I would've tried to convince my kids that these were good by saying, "Just add some salsa! How about more guacamole? They're not *that* bad." Not anymore; I've stopped pretending.

I used to pretend that the way I ate was for health reasons, but the way I ate very likely bordered on orthorexia (an obsession with eating healthy food). Once, I even brought chocolate mousse to a family party and was so excited that it was made with tofu, virtually fat-free, and had no dairy! Bless my family for trying it and pretending it tasted good. Blech.

If it doesn't taste good, don't try choking down imposter foods in the name of "health." Health isn't binary. It happens on a spectrum and includes mental, physical, and spiritual aspects of health as opposed to the diet industry's emphasis on the physical only part of the health definition. How many of your food choices are based on "health" and a desire to lose weight?

YOLO.

And no offense, Maria and Ricardo, but we aren't wasting our bites on those quinoa tortillas (unless, of course, you're gluten-free and need to find a way to make these palatable...then I recommend cheese. A LOT of cheese). At least we saved the meal with Mi Nina chips and some homemade guacamole. And ice cream. Taco Tuesday shall return in style once we can source our beloved flour tortillas.

I encourage you to take some time this week and go through your refrigerator and pantry and get rid of that fat-free cottage cheese, those snack puffs, and anything else you're eating that you don't truly like and are only consuming for the sake of weight loss or weight maintenance. Toss it all and replace the food with things you really crave and love. Life is too short to be plugging your nose and downing shots of apple cider vinegar.

Summary

Take some time this week to think about what foods actually taste good in your body. What gives you energy? What brings you joy? If weight didn't matter, what would you choose to eat just because it's what your body craved and you enjoyed? Is there any particular food in your home you don't even like to eat but have on hand because you think you "should" eat it at some point, if not daily (looking at your ground flaxseed)? How would it feel if you got rid of some traditional diet foods in your pantry or refrigerator? I encourage you to assess what's coming into your house and going into your body.

Mantra

- Eating food for the sake of weight loss isn't how I want to spend my time and energy.
- I can spend time finding foods that taste good and make my body feel good.
- I deserve to have my home filled with foods I love.

** I realize that I'm speaking from a place of privilege. I have enough money to get the food that our family wants and needs, and that's unfortunately not the case for millions of Americans. I encourage you to donate to your local food shelter or check out www.feedingamerica.org or the UN World Food Programme to learn about how you can help those struggling with food scarcity and insecurity.

Make Peace with Food

I never used to buy cookies or ice cream. No chance. I liked the idea of having these yummy foods but always felt out of control around them. If I had a weak moment at the grocery store and brought something "bad" home, I very likely would've put it into the rubbish bin outside in short order because I just couldn't trust myself.

Have you ever felt like food was calling your name? *"Come eat me; you know you can't ignore me any longer!"* *"I'm stronger than you are, and you know your willpower is ZERO!"* Being around certain foods made me feel uncomfortable, nervous, and anxious. In a word, I felt crazy. I couldn't have it, couldn't stop thinking about it, couldn't stop wanting it, couldn't stop wondering what the heck was wrong with me, and wondering when this weird food behavior would end. I just wanted to feel and be NORMAL around food.

Fast forward to today. My house is stocked with all the things. Cookies, ice cream, potato chips, granola bars, cereals, bagels, and breads. And here's the great part: I literally don't think about what's in the kitchen outside of checking to see what we've run out for my weekly grocery order. Sounds impossible to you? I promise it's not, and the way to make peace with food is probably not the solution you were thinking of and definitely doesn't involve a pantry padlock.

How do you really and truly feel peace around food? How will you no longer feel like food controls you or that you have no willpower? How do you stop seeing food as fake or real, red light or green light, healing or inflammatory, clean or dirty? Is it even possible to get rid of those food whispers that linger in your airwaves all day? The way to stop waging war against your body by using food as your weapon is to give yourself full and undeniable permission to eat whatever you want.

Permission to eat what you want, when you want, and the ability to see foods as neutral. That's it.

When you give full permission, like a genie granting wishes, and stop moralizing food like a religious zealot, you may feel like you are going for all the forbidden foods all the time. It's okay to have this "honeymoon" period where it's completely natural to want what you haven't had for weeks, months, or even years. Allow the process, and have patience. I promise that at some point, your body's intuition will ask for a fruit or vegetable eventually.

Don't be fooled into thinking that there'll be some magical day in the distance where you'll never want to eat sugary or high-carb foods ever again because you had this allowance period, because that day isn't coming. Fat activist and therapist Deb Burgard says we go from "dieting to donuts to discernment." When we stop dieting, we may want to eat donuts 24/7—and that's okay! Trust that there'll be a time when your body naturally expresses some level of discernment. *How do I feel when I eat certain foods? What really tastes good to me? If I know AND believe that the donuts are always available to me, do I want to eat them now or maybe later or maybe not at all?*

Sounds easy enough, but how do you know you've made peace with food? You'll know when you stop constantly thinking about food. You stop preventing yourself from eating what and how much that intuitive voice in your mind suggests. You stop shaming yourself for eating one or 10 of something. You'll greatly reduce your bingeing episodes because you won't be depriving yourself either physically or mentally. You'll discover that you don't even like some of the foods you used to "forbid" yourself from eating. And you also don't like some foods you ate freely because you thought they were "healthy" (hello, rice cakes and kale). No more last-supper mentality, meaning I have to eat it all today because the diet starts tomorrow! No more guilt. The general intensity you feel around food will decrease.

The bottom line here is to give yourself unconditional permission to eat whatever you want. If something looks appealing, go for it. Any food choice you make is emotionally equal to another. There is no shame or judgment if you choose to eat a carrot or if you choose to eat a piece of cake. Yes, the carrot and piece of cake are composed of different nutrients, but both give your body energy. Your worth and dignity remain 100% either way. By choosing the carrot, you aren't more noble, superior, or stronger than anyone who chooses the piece of cake. It's important to remember that unless you have unlimited access to food and feel a sense of emotional safety around food, you won't be able to discern what it is you really like and what feels good for your body.

What if you still hear those diet rules in your head? Whenever you have (or impose for your kids) rules around food, there usually comes a point when you inevitably break a rule. Once the rule has been broken, you tend to overeat with the "off the wagon" or "screw it" mentality. This leads to feeling shame and guilt, and you think you have proof that you have a problem with food (I knew I was just too weak and had no willpower) and now have to double down on your efforts to diet or restrain more, which brings you right back to step one...a new diet and the subsequent endless loop.

To get off the endless dieting loop, ask yourself this very important question: *Can I give myself the gift of unconditional permission?*

This doesn't look like, "Yes, I will eat this, but only if my weight is X." Or "Yes, I'll eat this and then run 5 miles tomorrow." Think about all foods as being equal. Wipe the slate clean. Level the playing field, and from there, you can learn how to play the game that feels best to you and your body.

One challenge in giving yourself permission is that you'll likely uncover some underlying anxiety in your life. Remind yourself that this is normal and that disordered eating is rooted in anxiety. Gwenyth Olwyn, an eating disorder researcher, teaches that eating disorders are really the misidentification of food as a threat. There's a great deal of research that points to both genetics and anxiety playing a significant role in those who develop eating disorders. Even if you were never diagnosed as having an eating disorder, if you've never felt at peace around food, there's a decent chance there's some level of anxiety in your life. I'm not a doctor and not diagnosing anyone with this statement, but I feel it's important to mention because it really helped me understand that it wasn't my fault and that I wasn't broken. I was simply responding to my inner wiring, which was triggered when I fell below my body's baseline for energy requirements.

The bottom line of this section is that recovery from disordered eating is possible. Even if you've been a lifelong or years-long dieter, you don't have to continue feeling like a crazy person around food. Take some time to reconnect with your body. Trust yourself. Give full allowance and permission. Remind yourself that there are no rules and no behavior around food is wrong. Give up on control as a method. Adopt the feeling of hopelessness when it comes to diets, but never give up hope on yourself or your ability to heal. Relax.

SUMMARY

The way to stop feeling crazy around food isn't to tighten up on diet measures like restricting, eliminating, or avoiding. To feel at peace and relaxed around food, consider letting go of any preconceived truths about what you're supposed to eat. Focus on listening to your body and letting your body guide you toward what foods you want and how much you need. There's no moral superiority gained by eating certain foods so take time to get to know what tastes and feels good in your body. Trust the experience of loosening your grasp, even if you notice loosening this grip awakens some anxiety. According to Gwenyth Olwyn, anxiety is at the root of many disordered eaters, so know that when food can't be used to control your fears or feelings (yes, you've given up hope on dieting), you might notice your anxiety presenting in different ways in your life. Easing anxiety, managing your stress, and giving up control will be big parts of your anti-diet journey.

* * *

MANTRA

- I can relax around food by giving myself full allowance around food.
- I can relax knowing that my body will guide me toward the type and amount of foods it needs.
- I can trust my body's signals.
- It's possible to find peace and feel relaxed around food now and forever.

Afterword

I want to thank you for joining me on this journey of self-discovery when it comes to food and your body. Yes, this book is about what to do for your kids, but it's also a guide for yourself.

First and foremost, remember to trust yourself and trust your kids. Let them make mistakes and learn from their own experiences. Eating is a way for both you and your kids to exert your free will and make choices for yourself.

There's no shame or guilt in where you are right now or where you've been in the past. We've all had periods of funky, weird, crazy, wacky things we've tried in the name of "health." When we know better, we can do better. Now that you have more tools and under-standing about food, body, and health, you can begin this journey fresh on a new path.

Expect twists and turns. Expect the path to be difficult at times. Not everybody knows the truths in this book, and that's okay. You can stay your course, knowing that your path is the one that will give you the best chance at true physical, mental, and emotional health and well-being.

There will be no "arrival" gate to enter. You simply know that you've "departed" the diet culture world on a one-way ticket. You might be tempted to return, but you know the likely outcome and will, hopefully, think twice about any return availability.

As you continue swimming through diet culture waters, expect to feel triggered, expect that old habits around food and body sometimes take a long time to loosen their grip, and also expect to feel better than you thought possible. Expect that you'll have a new perspective that will give you back so much of your time, your energy, your vitality, your resources, both financial and physical, and your sanity. Expect to feel surprised at how good and normal it feels to stop obsessing about food and your body and live the precious time you have on this planet fully present in body and mind.

I'll be here cheering you on from afar and know that finding peace and freedom around food and your body is possible.

Acknowledgments

I want to thank so many anti-diet warriors who've gone before me and taught me what I know. Many of them are listed in my resources section, but these ladies deserve special thanks. I'm forever grateful to Isabel Foxen Duke for mentoring and certifying me and for helping thousands of women come to peace with food and their body. I've also learned so much about body image through Summer Innanen. Christy Harrison's work has been incredibly impactful on my journey as well.

This book wouldn't be possible without the support of my loving husband and the most amazing six kids in the world. I want to thank my family for putting up with my writing early in the morning, late at night, on airplanes, on vacations, and everywhere in between! Having your support meant everything, and I hope this book serves our family and generations of our family to come. You're my greatest source of pride and inspiration, and I love you all more than you'll ever know.

Special thanks to my parents for their unwavering support and love, and my sister and family and friends who supported me both near and far, not only in the writing of this book but during the years when I wasn't a "normal" eater. Being loved unconditionally is a true gift.

Extra thanks to Alexandra Franzen, who inspired me to be a better human and writer and helped me bring my first dream book into the world. My editor, Kayla, and the entire team at Get It Done helped make my second dream book reality with constant support, editing, and encouragement. Kayla, thank you for believing this book and my message mattered. You have a true gift, and this book would not have been possible without you.

Resources

For links to the resource section, please visit www.andreadow.com/resources.

* * *

Jes Baker, author and blogger behind The Militant Baker, has curated an incredible list of ways to diversify your IG feed. Jes has lived experience in a larger body, and I highly recommend her book, *LandWhale*.

http://www.themilitantbaker.com/2017/04/diversify-your-instagram-feed.html?utm_source=convertkit&utm_medium=email&utm_campaign=How+You+Can+Tell+Diet+Culture+from+True+Recovery+-+7816921&m=1

* * *

HELPFUL PEOPLE

80+ Eating Disorder and Body Image Providers and Activists
https://www.threebirdscounseling.com/single-post/2018/03/18/Diversity-Is-A-Good-Thing-80-Eating-Disorder-Body-Image-Providers-Activists

Christy Harrison's list of HAES dieticians and therapists
https://christyharrison.com/haes-anti-diet-intuitive-eating-providers-eating-disorder-recovery

* * *

HEALTH AT EVERY SIZE (HAES) RESOURCES

Health at Every Size website:
https://sizediversityandhealth.org/content.asp?id=19

Look for HAES professionals in your area
https://sizediversityandhealth.org/

HAES letter to your healthcare provider

http://mosaiccarenc.com/wp-content/uploads/2019/02/Letter-to-Healthcare-provider-Weight-inclusive-Care.pdf

An excellent one-page resource to bring to your doctor that describes HAES and how you want to approach your medical treatment.

Health at Every Size eating disorder treatment facilities

Opal Food + Body Wisdom in Seattle
https://www.opalfoodandbody.com/

Center For Discovery
https://centerfordiscovery.com/

More HAES resources from Isabel Foxen Duke

The war on 'prediabetes' could be a boon for pharma—but is it good medicine?
https://www.science.org/content/article/war-prediabetes-could-be-boon-pharma-it-good-medicine

Critical Interview with Christy Harrison & Ragen Chastain

https://christyharrison.com/foodpsych/4/how-to-fight-back-against-weight-stigma-with-ragen-chastain

Obesity and Joint Replacement

https://wellroundedmama.blogspot.com/2017/07/obesity-and-joint-replacement-part-1.html?m=1

10 Reasons I Ditched Dieting

https://danceswithfat.org/2016/02/04/10-reasons-i-ditched-dieting/

The Weight-Inclusive vs. The Weight-Normative Approach
https://www.hindawi.com/journals/jobe/2014/983495/

Big Fat Lies by Glenn Gaesser
https://www.amazon.com/Big-Fat-Lies-Weight-Health/dp/0936077425

The Obesity Myth by Paul Campos
https://www.amazon.com/Obesity-Myth-Americas-Obsession-Hazardous/dp/1592400663

This Poodle Analogy Perfectly Illuminates the Problem with Fatphobia in Society
https://everydayfeminism.com/2015/09/poodle-science-haes/

What "Everybody Knows" About Fat People
https://danceswithfat.org/2015/10/01/what-everybody-knows-about-fat-people/

Lies They Told Me About Health by Ragen Chastain
https://danceswithfat.org/2014/10/29/lies-they-told-me-about-health/

Our Absurd Fear of Fat
https://www.nytimes.com/2013/01/03/opinion/our-imaginary-weight-problem.html

For Fat Patients and Their Doctors
https://danceswithfat.org/2012/04/21/for-fat-patients-and-their-doctors/

Athletic vs. Fit vs. Healthy
https://danceswithfat.org/2014/06/22/marathon-update-marathon-vs-health-vs-fitness/

If You Are Fat and Sick
https://danceswithfat.org/2015/10/05/if-you-are-fat-and-sick/

Dear Virgie: "My Doctor is Fatphobic"
http://bit.ly/1DGnRfg

Fat People and Our Knees
https://danceswithfat.org/2015/05/20/fat-people-and-our-knees/

Fat People and Tax Dollars
https://danceswithfat.org/2014/01/15/fat-people-and-tax-dollars/

The Weight-Inclusive versus Weight-Normative Approach to Health: Evaluating the Evidence for Prioritizing Well-Being over Weight Loss
https://www.hindawi.com/journals/jobe/2014/983495/

Mindful Eating for Bariatric Surgery
https://amihungry.com/programs/mindful-eating-for-bariatric-surgery

Mindful Eating for Prediabetes and Diabetes
https://amihungry.com/programs/mindful-eating-for-diabetes

When we talk about weight loss research
https://danceswithfat.org/2017/01/24/when-we-talk-about-weight-loss-research/

Family Therapy resource:
F.E.A.S.T. or family-based therapy resource center
https://www.feast-ed.org/what-is-family-based-treatment/

* * *

MORE MODELS/PEOPLE TO FOLLOW FROM ISABEL FOXEN DUKE

First off, Bustle Magazine put together this really, amazing list of BoPo accounts to follow.
https://www.bustle.com/articles/39160-23-plus-size-bloggers-to-follow-on-instagram-for-all-the-fashion-food-and-beauty-inspo-you

BuzzFeed put together this list of plus-size yogis to follow; and here are some more plus-size fitness people to follow by Bustle.
https://www.bustle.com/articles/165647-13-plus-size-fitness-babes-on-instagram-who-will-inspire-your-movement-practice-photos

And here are some of my personal fave people to follow:

IFD Bodies (a curation of images by yours truly—feel free to click through and follow any of the models you like on this page!)
https://www.instagram.com/ifd_bodies

Gabi Fresh
https://www.instagram.com/gabifresh

Nola Trees
https://nolatreeproject.org

Bonjour Clem
https://www.instagram.com/bonjourclem

The Adipositivity Project
https://www.instagram.com/adipositivity

Virgie Tovar
https://www.virgietovar.com

Denise Bidot
https://www.instagram.com/denisebidot

Jessamyn Stanley
https://jessamynstanley.com

Nadia Aboulhosn
https://www.instagram.com/nadiaaboulhosn

Tess Holliday (largest plus model to be signed to major agency)
https://www.instagram.com/tessholliday

Margie Plus (Lena Dunham is obsessed with her.)
https://instagram.com/margieplus/

19 Badass Instagrammers Who Prove Yoga Bodies Come In All Shapes And Sizes
https://www.buzzfeed.com/carolynkylstra/curvy-yoga

http://vimeo.com/94364919 (awesome music vid with three of my fave/most awesome plus-size models in the biz)

319

MEDIUM-SIZED WOMEN

Body Positive Panda (medium-sized non-model/activist/ED survivor)
https://instagram.com/bodyposipanda/

Bo Stanley (medium-sized woman; sometimes says slightly un-body-positive things, but
    if you're medium-sized or smaller her photos may be helpful)
https://instagram.com/bostanley/

Healthy Is the New Skinny (I don't love the name of this, but they have some great
    "medium-sized" plus-size models in their agency for those of you who are into that.
    Also a great "medium-sized" Instagram feed.)
http://healthyisthenewskinny.com

* * *

MY FAVORITE ANDROGYNOUS PLUS MODELS

https://www.instagram.com/beefcakeswimwear/

https://www.instagram.com/petipuasaturno/

https://www.instagram.com/samdylanfinch/
(More about documenting their ED recovery journey as a trans person, not as much about
    celebrating their own body—but great nonetheless)

* * *

MY FAVORITE MALE PLUS MODELS

https://www.instagram.com/p/B7rLX2spd6X/

https://www.instagram.com/extra_inches_plussizeblog/

https://www.instagram.com/steven_martin_plussize/

https://www.instagram.com/abearnamedtroy/

https://www.instagram.com/marquimode/

* * *

RESOURCES TO HELP MAKE THE WORLD A LITTLE EASIER TO NAVIGATE WHEN IT COMES TO WEIGHT AND SIZE

Dealing with airline seat reservations
https://danceswithfat.org/2019/04/17/us-airline-customer-of-size-policies/

AllGo app:
https://canweallgo.com/
AllGo is a review app where plus-size people rate the comfort and accessibility of public spaces so others can know what to expect. Their tagline is "We help people of size go out more, with less anxiety."

Is It Ample website:
https://www.isitample.com/
A review app to help people find all sorts of establishments that are friendly to marginalized bodies.

Buzzfeed Roundup to Handle Thigh Rub:
https://www.buzzfeed.com/augustafalletta/13-ways-to-deal-with-hot-sweaty-thighs-during-the-summer

Curvy Cupid Course:
https://www.curvycupidcourse.com/
Course for plus-size dating with Krista Niles

HEALTH & WELLNESS & MOVEMENT

Advice on dealing with doctors
https://betterhumans.coach.me/the-complete-guide-to-becoming-your-own-medical-advocate-ddc658a10a57

321

HAES letter to your healthcare provider

http://mosaiccarenc.com/wp-content/uploads/2019/02/Letter-to-Healthcare-provider-
   Weight-inclusive-Care.pdf

An excellent one-page resource to bring to your doctor that describes *HAES* and how you
   want to approach your medical treatment.

Fit Fatties

https://www.facebook.com/groups/fitfatties/

Reagan Chastain's Fit Fatties Forum on Facebook. No diet or weight loss talk, just fun
   posts about fitness.

Insight Timer

https://apps.apple.com/us/app/insight-timer-meditation-app/id337472899

FREE meditation app, mental health *is* physical health!

Green Mountain at Fox Run

https://www.fitwoman.com/?mc_cid=1bb2b922bc&mc_eid=1bc7368f0f

A whole-body wellness retreat in Vermont.

YOGA

Andrea Dow—MindBody YogaFlow

http://www.andreadow.com/mindbodyyogaflow

Dianne Bondy

https://diannebondyyoga.com/

Rachel Estapa

https://www.moretoloveyoga.com/

* * *

BODY POSITIVE EXERCISE PROGRAMS

Jill Angie of Not Your Average Runner coaches women of all sizes and abilities to become runners. Run your first 5K or take it to the next level with her monthly membership. She's a fellow certified coach and teaches the model, too!
https://notyouraveragerunner.com/

Body Exchange—Canada locations
http://bodyexchange.ca

* * *

CRISIS RESOURCES

National Hopeline Network (Crisis Hotline)
1-800-SUICIDE
1-800-784-2433

National Suicide Prevention Hotline
1-800-273-TALK
1-800-273-8255

Crisis Text Line
Text HOME to
U.S.: 741741
Canada: 686868
UK: 85258

Grief Support Hotline
1-650-321-5273

Eating Disorder Hotline
1-847-831-3438

Talk Space
www.talkspace.com

Talkspace is a website where, for a monthly fee, you can communicate with your choice of hundreds of therapists to whatever extent you feel comfortable with.

* * *

HEALTH AT EVERY SIZE EATING DISORDER TREATMENT FACILITIES

Opal Food + Body Wisdom in Seattle
https://www.opalfoodandbody.com/

Center For Discovery
https://centerfordiscovery.com/

* * *

CLOTHING RESOURCES

TomBoy X
https://tomboyx.com/
Underwear for everyone.

On the Plus Side
https://www.ontheplusside.com/
Plus-size fashion for sizes 2X to 8X.

Alice Alexander
https://alicealexander.co/
Beautiful hand-sewn clothing in sizes 0 to 28.

Old Navy
https://oldnavy.gap.com
Popular rockstar legging

Day Won
https://day-won.com/
Good for active wear!

Super Fit Hero

https://superfithero.com/

Good for active wear!

Girlfriend Collective

https://www.girlfriend.com/

This company is so cool. Not only do they have sizes XXS to 6XL, but they make their
leggings, sports bras, and other athletic clothing from recycled water bottles.

Torrid

https://www.torrid.com/

Forever 21

https://www.forever21.com/us/shop/catalog/category/plus/plus_size-sale

Anthroplogie's new A+ line

https://www.anthropologie.com/help/aplus

Venus

https://www.venus.com/plus-size.aspx

Smart Glamour

https://smartglamour.com/

I love that they show models in all sizes on their website!

Fashion For Fat Girls

https://bust.com/style/11900-fashion-for-fat-girls-spring-style.html

Plus Equals

https://www.plusequals.co.uk/

British made, up to size 24, size-inclusive models.

ASOS

https://www.asos.com/women/curve-plus-size/cat/?cid=9577&nlid=ww|cloth-
ing|shop+by+range

Nordstrom

https://shop.nordstrom.com

Vineyard Vines
https://www.vineyardvines.com

Swimsuits For All
https://www.swimsuitsforall.com

Universal Standard
https://www.universalstandard.com/

OKKO
http://www.loveokko.co

See Rose Go
http://www.seerosego.com

Smart Glamour
https://smartglamour.com/

The Plus Bus
https://www.instagram.com/theplusbus/
Fat positive online 24/7 at Poshmark and storefront in LA.

WRAY
XXS to 6XL sizing

Nettle Studios
XXS to 6XL sizing

Ember and Ace
https://www.emberandace.com/

Plus-size activewear for kids
Swimsuit options: Lands End, Torrid, Eloquii, Swimsuits for All

Clothing recycle resource
https://trashisfortossers.com/how-to-recycle-old-clothing/

PODCASTS

Interview with Deb Burgard

https://www.youtube.com/watch?v=n3lsfK2vM9k

Isabel Foxen Duke with Laura Thomas on body love and body acceptance

http://www.laurathomasphd.co.uk/podcast/ep75-w-isabel-foxen-duke/

Jessi Haggerty (she has many great interviews) interviews Isabel Foxen Duke

https://www.jessihaggerty.com/blog/blp30

Raising Kids with Body Trust- Hilary Kinavy

https://christyharrison.com/foodpsych/4/building-body-positive-families-hilary-kinavey

"Dear Sugars"- Trust Your Body

https://www.nytimes.com/2018/06/09/podcasts/listen-to-dear-sugars-trust-your-body-with-hilary-kinavey-dana-sturtevant.html

Linda Bacon, The Body Manifesto Video Series

https://lindabacon.org/videos/

Melissa Toler on Wild Mystic Woman Podcast

Opting Out of Diet Culture and Reclaiming Our Wellness

http://laylafsaad.com/wild-mystic-woman-podcast/016-melissa-toler

Christy Harrison's Food Psych—I have listened to EVERY episode and love them all. My personal favorites: Isabel Foxen Duke, Intuitive Eating (Evelyn Trebole and Elise), Body Positive (Connie and Elizabeth), Emily Contois, Alan Levinovitz, Marcie Evans.

https://christyharrison.com/foodpsych/

These are all gems, but this one with Ragen Chastain is a MUST LISTEN!

https://christyharrison.com/foodpsych/4/how-to-fight-back-against-weight-stigma-with-ragen-chastain

Julie Duffy Dillon—HAES dietitian and PCOS expert

http://www.juliedillonrd.com/

Body Kindness podcast with Rebecca Stritchfield—I especially liked the episode with Anna Lutz on talking about food and bodies with kids.

https://www.bodykindnessbook.com/podcast/

https://www.bodykindnessbook.com/2018/09/04/episode-92-talking-about-food-and-bodies-in-the-home-with-anna-lutz-rdn/

Another episode with Anna Lutz on raising intuitive eaters. Must listen if you have kids!
https://www.positive-nutrition.com/post/2017/05/09/65-raising-intuitive-eaters

Tabitha Farrar podcast (discontinued in 2019), she also does some lives on YouTube
https://eatingdisorderrecoverypodcast.podbean.com

She's All Fat podcast
https://shesallfatpod.com/

Virgie Tovar's Rebel Eaters Club podcast
https://www.rebeleatersclub.com

Tabitha Farrar's Eating Disorder Recovery podcast (discontinued in 2019)
https://eatingdisorderrecoverypodcast.podbean.com

Virginia Sole-Smith's Burnt Toast podcast has some great episodes with kid's focus
https://podcasts.apple.com/gb/podcast/burnt-toast-by-virginia-sole-smith/id1598931199

Sunny Side Up Nutrition podcast
https://sunnysideupnutrition.com/podcast/

Maintenance Phase—debunking "wellness" and weight loss.
https://www.maintenancephase.com/

PREGNANCY RESOURCES

Tips for Navigating Pregnancy and the Postpartum Period In Eating Disorder Recovery, Lauren Hill
https://www.theeatingdisordercenter.com/blog/tips-for-navigating-pregnancy-and-the-postpartum-period-in-eating-disorder-recovery

How to Have a Healthy Body Image During Pregnancy, Crystal Karges, RD
https://www.crystalkarges.com/blog/how-to-have-a-healthy-body-image-during-
pregnancy

**Fearless Rebelle Radio #130: Pregnancy, Body Image and Postpartum—Rachel Cole
and Summer Innanen**
https://summerinnanen.com/130/

https://www.middriftmovement.com/

http://thehonestbodyproject.com/

The Radical Doula

* * *

RETREATS

Green Mountain at Fox Run in Vermont
https://www.fitwoman.com/?mc_cid=1bb2b922bcandmc_eid=1bc7368f0f

Plus Size Birth with Jen McClellan
https://plussizebirth.com/about/

Nicola Salmon—Feminist and Fat Positive Fertility Coach
http://nicolasalmon.co.uk

* * *

ARTICLES

Your Body Is Not Your Masterpiece by Glennon Doyle Melton
https://www.huffpost.com/entry/your-body-is-not-your-masterpiece_b_5586341

Why I Stopped Selling Weight Loss by Melissa Toler
https://www.melissatoler.com/blog/why-i-stopped-selling-weight-loss

Go Ahead. Eat Your Holiday Feelings by Christy Harrison

https://www.nytimes.com/interactive/2019/11/23/opinion/sunday/emotional-eating-holidays.html

How Do You Feel About Your Body by Emma Pattee

https://www.nytimes.com/2019/05/24/learning/how-do-you-feel-about-your-body.html

Linda Bacon, Ph.D., author of *Health at Every Size and Body Respect* wrote these letters that you can share with friends and family and healthcare providers

https://lindabacon.org/HAESbook/pdf_files/HAES_For-Friends-and-Family.pdf

51 Ways to Make the World Less Hostile to Fat People

https://broadly.vice.com/en_us/article/mb4e7n/how-to-treat-fat-people-ally-fatphobia

Sugar Is Addictive? BS, These Health Pros Say by Anna Maderis Miller

https://health.usnews.com/wellness/food/articles/2018-11-16/sugar-is-addictive-bs-these-health-pros-say?src=usn_fb

No, Sugar Isn't The New Heroin by Traci Mann

http://behavioralscientist.org/no-sugar-isnt-new-heroin/

www.yourfatfriend.com

Your Fat Friend writes about the social realities of living as a large person.

What To Say To Kids About Sugar

https://wtop.com/news/2019/01/what-to-say-to-kids-about-sugar/

I Help People Recover From Disordered Eating. Don't Give This App To Your Child by Christy Harrison

https://www.nytimes.com/2019/08/18/opinion/weight-watchers-kids.html

Fat Is Not The Problem- Fat Stigma Is by Linda Bacon

https://blogs.scientificamerican.com/observations/fat-is-not-the-problem-fat-stigma-is/

How Weight Bias Is Harming Us All

https://theconversation.com/amp/how-weight-bias-is-harming-us-all-107352

10 Reasons Not To Focus On Your Weight In The New Year
https://www.pdxmonthly.com/articles/2016/12/27/ten-reasons-not-to-focus-on-your-weight-in-the-new-year

A Guide To Parenting Fat Kids
https://fluffykittenparty.com/2018/07/08/a-guide-to-parenting-fat-kids/

Thin White Men And Rebranding Diet Culture
https://www.bitchmedia.org/article/well-actually-wellness/thin-white-men-and-rebranding-diet-culture/3

Why You Gain Belly Fat After Menopause (And Why It's Ok) by Jessi Haggerty
https://www.jessihaggerty.com/blog/why-you-gain-belly-fat-after-menopause-and-why-its-ok

The Short Term Weight Loss Lie by Ragen Chastain
https://danceswithfat.org/2018/12/30/the-short-term-weight-loss-lie/

Big Fat Lies About Obesity
https://asunow.asu.edu/20190129-discoveries-big-fat-lies-about-obesity

We'll Never Achieve True Wellness If We're All Too Hungry To Get The Job Done
https://metro.co.uk/2019/06/29/well-never-achieve-true-wellness-if-were-all-hungry-to-get-the-job-done-10082343/

Raising Girls With Better Body Image FAQs
https://beautyredefined.org/raising-girls-body-image-faqs/

How To Make Kids Comfortable In Their Own Bodies by Melinda Wenner Moyer
https://slate.com/human-interest/2019/01/child-body-image-advice-weight-shaming.html

Great information on the reality of food addiction—a mix of blogs, podcasts, books, and webinars
https://www.joseesovinskynutrition.com/blog/food-addiction-resources

To Those Who Want Your Fat Family Member to Lose Weight
https://medium.com/personal-growth/to-those-who-want-your-fat-family-member-to-lose-weight-90c98fa19250

10 Principles of Intuitive Eating
https://www.intuitiveeating.org/10-principles-of-intuitive-eating/

Evelyn Tribole on Food Addiction
http://www.intuitiveeating.org/category/food-addiction/

Isabel Foxen Duke—What is Intuitive Eating and What is Health at Every Size? And Is Sugar Physically Addictive?
https://isabelfoxenduke.com/intuitive-eating/
https://isabelfoxenduke.com/health-at-every-size-haes/
https://isabelfoxenduke.com/is-sugar-physically-addictive-lets-discuss-2/

A Draft Agenda For Fat Justice
https://medium.com/@thefatshadow/a-draft-agenda-for-fat-justice-db878d93cd98

Kelsey Miller on Intuitive Eating
https://cupofjo.com/2018/11/kelsey-miller-intuitive-eating/

Chris Kresser on Chronic Illness and Acceptance
https://chriskresser.com/living-with-chronic-illness-the-power-of-acceptance/

Weight Discrimination and the Risk of Mortality
https://www.ncbi.nlm.nih.gov/pubmed/26420442

When You're Told You're Too Fat To Get Pregnant
https://www.nytimes.com/2019/06/18/magazine/fertility-weight-obesity-ivf.html

Smash The Wellness Industry by Jessical Knoll...A MUST READ!
https://www.nytimes.com/2019/06/08/opinion/sunday/women-dieting-wellness.html

Let's Talk about Thin Privilege by Melissa Fabello
https://everydayfeminism.com/2013/10/lets-talk-about-thin-privilege/

Medicare's Search for Effective Obesity Treatments: Diets Are Not the Answer
Trigger warning that, like any medical research paper, there's use of the "O" words, weights, and calories.
https://escholarship.org/uc/item/2811g3r3

Probability of an Obese Person Attaining Normal Body Weight
Trigger warning: Use of BMI and "O" words
https://www.ncbi.nlm.nih.gov/pmc/articles/PMC4539812/

Adios Barbie—website focused on size inclusivity and inclusion
http://www.adiosbarbie.com/

The Body Is Not An Apology —Sonya Renee Taylor
https://thebodyisnotanapology.com/

Everything You Know About Obesity Is Wrong
https://highline.huffingtonpost.com/articles/en/everything-you-know-about-obesity-is-
    wrong/

Dubious Diagnosis- the problem with prediabetes diagnosis
https://science.sciencemag.org/content/363/6431/1026

Fat Hygiene Must Haves by J Aprileo
https://comfyfat.com/2018/02/22/fat-hygiene-must-haves/

List of Body Affirming Children's Books
https://www.threebirdscounseling.com/single-post/2018/01/27/Body-Affirming-Children-
    Books-That-Teach-Kids-to-Trust-Celebrate-Their-Bodies

The body politic: the relationship between stigma and obesity-associated disease or
    this article (same researcher)
https://www.ncbi.nlm.nih.gov/pmc/articles/PMC2386473/
https://bmcpublichealth.biomedcentral.com/articles/10.1186/1471-2458-8-128

Hane's "Every Body" campaign
https://www.marketingdive.com/news/hanes-pushes-body-positivity-in-every-bod-
    campaign/560403/

* * *

VIDEOS & TED TALKS

Shrinking Women—Lily Meyers
https://www.youtube.com/watch?v=zQucWXWXp3k

The Space between Self-Esteem and Self-Compassion—Kristin Neff
https://www.youtube.com/watch?v=IvtZBUSplr4

Change Your World, Not Your Body—Jes Baker
https://www.youtube.com/watch?v=iSjwdN9vW0g

Body Trust is a Birthright—Dana Sturtevant and Hilary Kinavey
https://www.youtube.com/watch?v=aPUH3Hp1t9k

The Power of Vulnerability—Brene Brown
https://www.youtube.com/watch?v=iCvmsMzlF7o

Virgie Tovar's Lose Hate Not Weight TEDx Talk (she discusses many of these topics
    in her book)
https://www.youtube.com/watch?v=hZnsamRfxtY

Looks aren't everything, believe me, I'm a model
https://www.ted.com/talks/cameron_russell_looks_aren_t_everything_be-
    lieve_me_i_m_a_model

Why Dieting Doesn't Usually Work- Sandra Aamodt
https://www.ted.com/talks/sandra_aamodt_why_dieting_doesn_t_usually_work#t-43146

ABC's Modern Family Summary of Cam's Phases of Dieting
https://www.youtube.com/watch?v=ejfnle5lggM

Johann Hari's Ted Talk about addiction
https://www.ted.com/talks/johann_hari_everything_you_think_you_know_about_addic-
    tion_is_wrong

Victoria Welsby Ted Talk—How To Be Confident and Love Your Body At Any Size
https://www.youtube.com/watch?v=w_Ml3yr32bU

The Problem with Poodle Science
https://www.youtube.com/watch?v=H89QQfXtc-k

* * *

BLOGS

Ragen Chastain
https://www.reddit.com/r/RagenChastain/

Isabel Foxen Duke
https://isabelfoxenduke.com/

The Body is Not an Apology
https://thebodyisnotanapology.com/

Jes Baker—The Militant Baker
http://www.themilitantbaker.com/

Jessi Haggerty
https://www.jessihaggerty.com/

Virginia Sole-Smith—Burnt Toast
https://virginiasolesmith.substack.com/

Christy Harrison
https://christyharrison.com/blog

Summer Innanen
https://summerinnanen.com/blog/

Sofie Hagen
https://www.sofiehagen.com/

Fiona Willer
https://healthnotdiets.com/apps/blog

* * *

BOOKS

Health at Every Size
Intuitive Eating
Body Respect
Body Trust
My Life Without Ed
More Than A Body: Your Body Is An Instrument, Not An Ornament
Fat?So!
You Have the Right to Remain Fat
Feeding the Healthy Family
The Beauty Myth
The Gluten Lie
Self-Compassion:The Proven Power of Being Kind to Yourself
FatShame
Shrill
Belly of the Beast
Lessons from the Fat-o-sphere
Landwhale
Why Dieting Makes Us Fat
Big Girl
Anti-Diet
Fearing the Black Body
Fat Talk: Parenting in the Age of Diet Culture
Reclaiming Body Trust: A Path to Healing and Liberation

Some favorite kid's books:
Celebrate Your Body
The Body Book
Her Body Can
Bodies Are Cool
Raising Body Positive Teens: A Parent's Guide to Diet-free Living, Exercise, and Body Image
No Weigh!: A Teen's Guide to Positive Body Image, Food, and Emotional Wisdom
Starfish

336

PEOPLE TO FOLLOW ON SOCIAL MEDIA

Virgie Tovar
https://www.instagram.com/virgietovar/

Anna Sweeney
https://www.instagram.com/dietitiananna/

Virginia Sole-Smith
https://www.instagram.com/v_solesmith/

Shira Rose
https://www.instagram.com/theshirarose/

Jessamyn Stanley
https://www.instagram.com/mynameisjessamyn/

Isabel Foxen Duke
https://www.instagram.com/isabelfoxenduke/

Tess Holliday (largest plus-size model to be signed to a major agency)
https://www.instagram.com/tessholliday/

Body Posipanda—Megan Crabbe
https://www.instagram.com/bodyposipanda/

Amanda Lacount—awesome teen hip hop dancer with a body positive message
#breakingthestereotype
https://www.instagram.com/amandalacount/

Maxine Ali—health, science and feminist writer, body image researcher
https://www.instagram.com/maxineali/

Summer Innanen—body image coach
https://www.instagram.com/summerinnanen/?hl=en

Dianne Bondy Yoga—plus size yoga instructor
https://www.instagram.com/diannebondyyogaofficial/?hl=en

Jes Baker—body image coach and author
https://www.instagram.com/themilitantbaker/?hl=en

Fourth Trimester Bodies Project
https://www.instagram.com/4thtribodies/?hl=en

The Body Is Not an Apology—Sonya Renee Taylor
https://www.instagram.com/thebodyisnotanapology/?hl=en

Fat Acceptance and Body Positive Facebook Groups
https://bodypositivecalgary.wordpress.com/2015/09/14/fat-acceptance-and-other-body-
  positive-facebook-groups/

Research Cited:

1. https://www.ncbi.nlm.nih.gov/pmc/articles/PMC5253095/?utm_source=convertkit&utm_medium=email&utm_campaign=The+Truth+About+That+New+%22Fat+But+Fit%22+Study%20-%205310211

2. https://nutritionj.biomedcentral.com/articles/10.1186/1475-2891-9-30

3. http://www.ncbi.nlm.nih.gov/sites/entrez/17469900 (link goes to study)

4. https://nutritionj.biomedcentral.com/articles/10.1186/1475-2891-10-9?utm_source=convertkit&utm_medium=email&utm_campaign=The+Truth+About+That+New+%22Fat+But+Fit%22+Study%20-%205310211

About the Author

Andrea is a mom of six kids, yoga and Pilates instructor, and weight neutral coach who is passionate about helping people stop feeling obsessed with food and disliking their body so they can finally feel at peace and enjoy a new sense of freedom. When she's not cheering from the sidelines, or watching a dance competition, she loves traveling with her family. She and her husband, 6 kids and 1 dog live in Massachusetts.

Milton Keynes UK
Ingram Content Group UK Ltd.
UKHW010725130923
428592UK00004B/268